S0-BDT-032

THE SCIENCE OF GEMS

THE SCIENCE OF GEMS

P. J. Fisher, F.G.A., F.R.S.A.

CHARLES SCRIBNER'S SONS · NEW YORK

A-9.66 [UJ]

Printed in the United States of America
Library of Congress Catalog Card Number 66-22665

To my wife

ACKNOWLEDGMENTS

The author wishes to thank the following for their kind advice and assistance in the preparation of this book: Robert Webster, Fellow of the Gemmological Association of Great Britain; A. Nagy, one of London's most progressive diamond cutters; De Beers Consolidated Mines Limited; and the Japan Pearl Exporters' Association.

The following photographs were taken by Ernest Scott: Figs. 20, 41, 71, 73, and 77. The color photographs following pages 32, 64, and 96 were taken by Geoffrey Harper, and the stones and mineral crystals displayed were kindly provided by C. R. Mathews. Figs. 50–52 were drawn by H. Rappl.

Acknowledgment is made to the following for permission to reproduce illustrations: the British Museum (Natural History) for Figs. 2, 6, and 9; Eric Bruton for Figs. 37, 63, and 64; De Beers Consolidated Mines Limited for Figs. 7, 22–27, 29–31, and for the color photograph following page 128, the Japan Pearl Exporters' Association for Figs. 53–61; the Jewelry Industry Council of New York for Figs. 32 and 33; A. Nagy for Figs. 62, 65, 68, and 69; the Radio Times Hulton Picture Library for Figs. 28 and 49; Robert Webster for Figs. 40, 43, 80–83, and 86–89; and Wide World Photos for Figs. 1, 34, 35, 36, 42, and 44–48.

CONTENTS

ILLUSTRATIONS

PREFACE

As far back as man's knowledge of history extends, he has always tried to add color and beauty to the merely useful things in life. Whether this is a wrought-iron gate at the entrance to a garden or the jewel-studded dagger of an Indian prince, even in designing utilitarian articles man endeavors, wherever possible, to mold and color the surfaces of his materials in order to give them a more pleasing and beautiful appearance. There is significance in this, for if we look at nature itself and recall, for instance, the sensations of pleasure experienced at the sight of a simple bouquet of flowers, we realize that what at first may appear purely decorative—and therefore useless—is really a necessary part of our existence, for without beauty life would indeed be dull and meaningless.

For thousands of years, gems have been used both for the adornment of the human person and for the decoration of *objets d'art.* They remain unchanged throughout the centuries, and man now uses them both in fashion and industry. Indeed, gems have influenced history, from their setting in a simple engagement ring—a token of promise and affection—to their appearance in royal crowns of fabulous value—symbols of power and authority.

Today, the mining, preparation, cutting, and marketing of gem stones has grown to such extensive proportions that in some countries it forms an important part of the economy. This has led to the development of a specialized branch of the science of *mineralogy,* the study of minerals, known as *gemmology,* or the scientific study of gem stones.

In this book I have tried to introduce the reader to the many aspects of this most fascinating subject.

P. J. FISHER

LONDON

THE SCIENCE OF GEMS

I

GEMS THROUGH HISTORY

It is difficult to say accurately how far back in history men first began to take an interest in gems, but it is likely to have been at the very dawn of man's development, for color is bound up with life at all stages, and the desire for and use of bright and colorful decorations are not, in fact, only the prerogative of man.

In the animal world, nature has produced some remarkable color combinations and designs, which are particularly conspicuous among some birds. Two of many examples are the colorful tail feathers of the peacock and the exquisite plumage of the birds of paradise. Such bright animal colors and designs have a number of straightforward biological functions, among which courtship, display, and defense are of major importance. Primitive man tried to simulate, with a variety of materials, what he saw in the jungle world around him and consequently adopted many of nature's decorations to fit his own behavior patterns. The ritual headdress of a tribal chief made from the feathers of jungle birds, bracelets and necklaces made from the teeth of animals, and the decorative use of beads and colored stones, all have significance and ritual meaning in the lives of many tribal societies.

Archaeologists and anthropologists who have studied the society and culture of early tribal communities have found ancient ornaments and jewelry of great assistance in determining whether the peoples who owned them were hunters, fishermen, or agriculturalists, and, by examination of the execution of the work, knowledge can be gained of how the technical skills of cutting and drilling stone and metal were developed.

The Magical Powers of Gem Stones

In the times before the Roman Empire, which began in 27 B.C., the value and significance of gem stones was dependent upon their specific color and general appearance, and no attempt had been made to classify them according to their mineral species. All stones of one color were probably considered to be of the same kind and therefore judged equally valuable. Today, particularly in Western society, gems are usually valued according to their beauty, durability, and rarity; but, to the men of ancient societies, it was not only the decorative aspects of jewels that made them important. Superstitions and ritual meaning attached to the colorful stones gave them much of their intrinsic value. The power of magic was ascribed to gem stones. They were not only reputed to cure diseases of all kinds, but, as amulets, they were carried about to ward off and protect the wearer against evil spirits, at the same time bringing good luck.

The belief in the medicinal powers of gem stones lasted well into the eighteenth century; up to this time they formed an important part of the doctor's medicinal chest. For example, an actual price list of a German druggist, printed in the second half of the eighteenth century, has been discovered. It gives details of the cost of different recipes containing gem stones to be used for medicinal purposes.

Pliny the Elder (A.D. 23–79), the famous Roman writer and natural historian, refers, among other stones, to the agate, a form of quartz, as a remedy for diseases of the eye. He even distinguishes between Indian and Egyptian agates, the former allegedly holding curative powers for diseases of the eye, while the latter were said to be effective against the bites of spiders and scorpions. The bloodstone, another of the numerous varieties of quartz, was used by ancient alchemists in treating disorders of the blood. It was supposed to be effective in the treatment of blood poisoning, and its application was believed to check the flow of blood from a wound. Emeralds were hung around the necks of children to protect them from epileptic fits, while powdered beryl was said to have special powers of healing when applied to injuries of the eye. Garnets, too, had a host of curative powers ascribed to them. Besides protecting the wearer against the effects of poisons of all kinds, they were also said to cure depressions and give protection against bad dreams. The red varieties were said to relieve fever, while yellow gems were prescribed for the treatment of jaundice.

Numerous other examples that describe the medicinal powers of gem stones can be found in ancient writings, and records prove that their influence over the lives of people must have been considerable. Any beneficial effects obtained from the use of gems must have been psychological, for none of these minerals could have had the slightest remedial effects on the ailments for which they were prescribed.

Belief in the magic, rather than curative, power of gem stones probably reached its height during the rule of the Roman emperors. In early Roman literature, there are many references to the power of gems to protect the owner against attacks from wild animals and safeguard him from the violence of robbers. Romantic associations were also ascribed to gem stones, and success in love, together with the power to read the thoughts of others, was said to belong to the possessor of precious stones.

In the fourteenth century, the Black Death (bubonic plague) swept over Europe, taking millions of lives. Those who were rich enough to afford it positively covered themselves with jewels of every description. It not only gave them self-confidence and made them forget their troubles and fears, but the belief was still strong that the purity of jewels would ward off pestilence.

The wearing of birth stones, another superstition, dates back to the early Middle Ages, but the belief originated far earlier. Indeed, it seems to have its source in the Bible story of the jeweled breast plate worn by the high priest. This breast plate, we are told, was set with twelve gems, each dedicated to a tribe of Israel. The actual identity of the stones, although they are named in the Bible, cannot be determined with any degree of certainty, because their names have changed over the centuries, and a number of differing lists describing them are extant. Later, when these gems became associated with the twelve signs of the zodiac, it was believed that if the proper jewel were worn at the right time, good luck would follow, or at least misfortune would be avoided. Ladies of noble birth wore the gem of the month, which necessitated their having twelve sets of jewelry. Those of lesser means had to make do with one set, and so it became customary to wear only the gem associated with the month of one's birth.

At first, the birth stone was worn in accordance with what was believed to be cabalistic instructions, but, in 1912, the American Association of Jewelers and Gem Merchants adopted the following list, selecting some of the more readily available stones.

January	Garnet
February	Amethyst
March	Bloodstone; alternative, aquamarine
April	Diamond
May	Emerald
June	Pearl; alternative, moonstone
July	Ruby
August	Sardonyx; alternative, peridot
September	Sapphire
October	Opal; alternative, tourmaline
November	Topaz
December	Turquoise; alternative, lapis lazuli

Though these superstitions have now nearly all vanished, some traces of them still remain. Even today it is said that the famous blue Hope diamond will bring misfortune to whoever owns it. There is, of course, no real basis for this belief, but it is understandable that the possession of a stone worth nearly $900,000 is bound to be somewhat awe-inspiring, and the responsibility of safeguarding it is rather frightening.

Legend says opals bring bad luck, and so strong is this belief that many people in our Western society will not tolerate opal jewelry in their homes, let alone wear it. Few realize that this superstition was born in comparatively recent times. It originated in a novel by the Scottish writer Sir Walter Scott, in *Anne of Geierstein,* published in 1829; he writes imaginatively about a beautiful lady and an evil opal. Later, Queen Victoria did much to overcome this superstition by presenting a fine collection of these stones to each of her daughters on the occasion of the girl's marriage. Yet the opal legend may well be based in part on the very nature of these stones; for example, they are easily liable to damage under certain circumstances. The scientific aspects of this fact are discussed in Chapter IV. How such superstitions may change over the centuries is well illustrated by the ways this beautiful stone was viewed in early documents, where it was described as a symbol of hope and purity that was able to protect its wearer against disease.

The History of Gems in Jewelry

It is difficult to write about the history of gem stones without becoming closely involved with the wider subject of jewelry and some of the metals used in its making. Just as gems form a part of the wider field of jewelry in general, so is jewelry itself a part of the artistic and religious spheres of various ages and civilizations. The true home of the art of jewelry making was the Orient, and it was from there that the craft spread to the Greek and Roman world. Yet it is wrong to imagine that the Western nations simply imitated oriental ideas without adding their own artistry and design. The Greeks, particularly, and, to a lesser extent the Etruscans and Romans, often achieved results in the design and execution of their work that surpassed that of their Eastern masters.

In order to trace some of this history, let us turn to ancient Egypt, where, as early as the Old Kingdom, beginning about 3200 B.C., craftsmen first modeled gold into exquisite ornaments. This precious element was the principal and favorite metal used in jewelry work, and with good reason. It had the value of being available only in small quantities, and, because gold is the only metal to occur in appreciable amounts in its native form, it could be put to use immediately without first having to be refined. Gold is also the most malleable and ductile of all metals and could thus be worked into intricate, artistic shapes with comparative ease. Its resistance to attack by most chemical substances is remarkable, and it retains its beautiful color and luster virtually forever. In the eyes of ancient civilizations, this attribute may well have given gold an almost supernatural quality.

The Egyptian artisans beat the gold on a flat stone with another stone held in the hand until it was transformed into a sheet of even thickness. The designs were then engraved on the back of the gold sheet with a hand punch; this process is known as *repoussé work.* Short pieces of wire could also be made from gold sheeting by cutting narrow strips off the edge and hammering and rolling them into a rounded form. When a longer piece of wire was required, it was made by cutting the gold sheet in the form of a spiral. The art of attaching tiny grains of gold to gold surfaces for decoration, known as *granulation,* was fully mastered by the Egyptians and was later also extensively used in Greek and Roman jewelry making. Much of Egyptian jewelry was also decorated with gem stones and colored glass. Among the former, quartz minerals, such as rock crystal, amethyst, agate, carnelian, and jasper were frequently used, but others, notably turquoise, beryl, feldspar, garnet, and lapis lazuli, were also somewhat popular.

In addition to its visual appeal, Egyptian jewelry always had symbolic meaning, and various designs were intimately bound up with traditions and religious beliefs. The most usual design was the scarab, a beetle that was a symbol of the resurrection of the dead. Carved in a variety of materials, including gem stones, scarab designs are to be found in many early Egyptian art forms. Clay pieces, colored cleverly to pass for turquoise and often set side by side with the natural gem, have also been found in ancient Egyptian jewelry, showing that even in those days men attempted to imitate gems.

Egyptian bead work was highly developed, and many bead ornaments were made from gems. While their use in jewelry was widespread, beads were also used as a convenient and easily manageable form of currency for trading purposes. Before about 700 B.C., when the use of money as we know it today was established, everything was bought and sold by barter. The use of gems, particularly in the form of beads, as currency for barter quickly spread to many nations, particularly those in the Mediterranean region, and ancient Egyptian beads have been found in many countries of the world. Even today, beads are still used as a means of exchange among the more primitive peoples of the world. Some Indian tribes of South America find a gift of colored-stone beads more acceptable to their taste than the dollar bill. Highly developed countries, too, regard gem stones as a kind of currency, that is, as a particularly safe financial investment, and when, in times of economic crisis, the value of money may become unstable, some people think that the most prudent investment of their resources lies in diamonds.

After the decline of Egypt, the Phoenicians became the principal traders in the Mediterranean regions, and oriental forms of art soon left their permanent impression in the classical lands. The early Greek jewelry of the eighth and seventh centuries B.C., known as the Orientalizing Period, is strongly influenced by Egyptian symbols and designs, but unlike the latter's form of art, which was strictly controlled by religion and custom, the Greeks allowed their craftsmen a free hand, and the symbolic significance of their work was thus considerably less pronounced.

Among the goldsmiths and jewelers of ancient civilizations, the Greeks hold front rank, and many fine examples of their delicate work can still be seen in museums all over the world. As with the Egyptians, gold was also the favorite metal of the Greek craftsmen, but a naturally occurring gold and silver alloy, known as electrum, was also used by them. The use of silver alone seems to have been restricted to cheaper jewelry. The decorative arts of filigree and granulation were highly developed. Early forms of *filigree* consisted of fine gold wires soldered in various patterns onto a solid gold background. This form of decoration has remained popular throughout the ages to the present day. Granulation gradually fell into disuse in Roman time and finally died out altogether. The secret of the ancient craftsmen who managed the feat of granulation, for which ordinary soldering methods are much too coarse, was only rediscovered by Henry Ambrose Pudsay Littledale in 1933.

Another form of decoration, known as *inlaying,* was practiced by the

Greeks. In this, colored gem stones and pieces of glass were cemented into metal cells made from gold strips soldered to a solid background. The art of *enameling* was also known to the craftsmen of the classical lands. For their raw materials they used powdered glass of various colors, which was placed into the area to be decorated and then fired. The heat caused the glass to melt and penetrate the softened metal to form the smooth and attractive coating associated with enamel work.

During the Hellenistic period, 330–27 B.C., the Greeks had extensive trade with Egypt and western Asia, and many colorful gem stones were imported from the East. The jewelry of this period was decorated with stones of various types, and the flesh-red form of chalcedony, known as carnelian, as well as the purple amethyst, were frequently to be seen. Pearls from the Mediterranean were popular in those days, too, but most popular of all were red garnets set in gold, a most attractive color combination that became fashionable again in Victorian times.

The use of gem stones in Greek jewelry was, however, limited, and those in rings and necklaces were either simple *cabochon cut,* a rounded dome shape, or were set in the various pieces in their natural crystalline shapes.

Just as Greek jewelry was strongly influenced by the work of Egyptian craftsmen, Roman jewelry was influenced by the Greeks and the Etruscans. Before the inauguration of the Roman Empire, all forms of jewelry in Republican Rome were considered to be luxuries and were disapproved of by the state. By 27 B.C., however, Rome had virtually become the master of the civilized world, and the old ideas of austerity were quickly forgotten. During the latter part of the Roman Empire, which lasted until A.D. 337, an increasing emphasis was placed on gem stones in jewelry for their own sake, and less care was taken with the gold work in which they were set. Here, for the first time, some of the hardest gem stones were used, and even uncut diamonds made their appearance. Particularly important were the emeralds that came from the Egyptian mines in the Red Sea hills. These stones were often set in jewelry in the natural hexagonal-crystal forms in which they were found.

Many famous emeralds of ancient times are carved with *intaglio* portraits, that is, the design is carved beneath the surface of the material. And the seal rings of kings and emperors were set with engraved emeralds. The famous first imperial seal of Augustus Caesar, the first Roman Emperor, is believed to have been the celebrated emerald belonging to the Greek ruler Alexander the Great. Napoleon Bonaparte is said to have given his wife Josephine a large emerald after his victorious Italian campaign. This is probably the oval gem, weighing 225 carats, now owned by a New York gem merchant. It is carved with the likeness of Julius Caesar.

Julius Caesar himself was an ardent collector of gems. He is reputed to have had a number of different groups of gem stones, which were displayed in the forum to the people of Rome.

In the days of the Roman Empire, most of the more common gem minerals had already been discovered. There are references in the literature of this period to a stone called *adamas* (invincible), which may well have been the diamond. The manner in which this stone was tested was extremely severe. It had to be placed on an anvil and struck with a hammer. If the blow shattered the crystal, it was proof that the stone was false, but if it withstood this treatment, it was the genuine adamas. Although the diamond is the hardest natural substance on earth, such a blow is almost certain to shatter it, and many a beautiful and rare crystal must have been destroyed through ignorance.

Even though in the days of the Roman Empire the austerities of Republican times had largely been forgotten and large sums of money were spent on extravagant pieces of personal jewelry for women, it was still considered effeminate for men to wear jewels, and many writers, including Pliny, severely attacked a growing trend to change the custom. Nevertheless, politicians and orators alike adorned their fingers with bejeweled rings to impress their audiences with their importance and high standing in society. Pliny also refers in his writings to the glass gems of the populace, and this explains one reason why Roman glass work was so highly developed and well-executed.

After the Roman Empire, in the Middle Ages—a term generally applied to the period from A.D. 476 to 1494—the use of sophisticated jewels and ornaments was very much on the increase. A strong link developed between the jewelers' craft and the church. The focus of art in those days was the church, and, therefore, most of the work of artists was in some way related to religious ideas. Many new churches and cathedrals were built all over Europe, and their altars and furnishings were richly embedded with gems and golden ornaments.

In the early part of this period, however, artistic design in all branches of the visual arts was again strongly influenced by an inrush of oriental ideas. Trade with the countries of western Asia was rapidly expanding, and with it came the knowledge of the magnificence and lavishness of oriental decorations. Gem stones of all kinds poured into Europe from the East, and their use in jewelry and ornamental designs lent color to the work of the craftsmen, which stood in sharp contrast with the delicate severity so pronounced in the earlier Greek work.

During the early years of the twelfth century, the first trade guilds were founded, and among them was the famous Goldsmiths' Guild of England. Disputes over the division of labor, very similiar to those occurring today, were known even in those early times. Thus, for example, only a goldsmith was allowed to work with the precious metals gold and silver. Craftsmen not observing this rule were liable to heavy fines.

The arts in Europe flourished during the fifteenth century. The Renaissance of this era began in Italy, and from that country new creative thoughts spread throughout Europe. Color was still of major importance in jewelry design, and the standard of workmanship remained high, so that the jewelry of this period was particularly attractive. Red rubies, blue sapphires, and fine green emeralds together with other gem stones and pearls, were mounted on gold and silver ornaments of all description. Much of the jewelry of the Renaissance was enameled, and some of this work is closely associated with the master goldsmith, Benvenuto Cellini (1500–1571), whose services were in great demand by the Church and the royal courts of Europe. At that time, the trade in precious stones is said to have been mostly in the hands of German and Dutch merchants who imported them from the Orient. In those days, since gem stones were chosen principally for their color and form, irregularities in shape did not detract from a stone's artistic value, and such gems were often incorporated in designs that suited their particular shape.

The art of diamond polishing had come into being only a relatively short time before, and partially polished diamond crystals began to appear more frequently in jewelry of that period. It has often been said that it was the Flemish gem cutter, Louis De Berquem of Bruges, who, in 1476, first discovered the secrets of how to cut and polish diamonds and thus bring out their true fire. This statement is only approximately true, for records show that, as early as 1412, the Duke of Burgundy possessed, in addition to a sizable diamond with lozenge-shaped facets, a table-cut diamond with large, mirrorlike facets. Moreover, even in the town of Bruges, the home of De Berquem, a number of gem cutters seem to have been engaged in diamond polishing in 1465, for they are referred to as diamond polishers in some legal documents of the time. It is perfectly clear, therefore, that diamond polishing actually was a well-established craft in De Berquem's time, and some authorities suggest it may have been known as early as 1370. De Berquem's particular claim to fame seems to lie in the suggestion that he was the first of the diamond cutters to recognize the importance of accurate geometrical faceting and thus laid the foundations for the *brilliant cut*—a special operation that allows for the maximum internal light reflection in a cut stone.

The art of diamond cutting soon spread to other leading cities in Europe, thus paving the way for the cities of Antwerp and Amsterdam to develop into two great centers of the diamond-cutting industry. Although Antwerp is still the greatest diamond-cutting center in the world, employing some fourteen thousand workers, in recent years other centers, notably Israel, are gaining in importance (see the table "Distribution of Diamond Workers Throughout the World, 1965," page 157).

During the sixteenth century, the appetite of the royal court of England for extravagant jewelry seems to have been insatiable. Henry VIII loved gems and jewels of every kind, and it is said that when he died he was the possessor of nearly six hundred brooches and rings that had richly adorned his person during his lifetime. So keen was his interest in jewelry that he was unable to resist salesmen who offered him their wares; it is possible that some unscrupulous dealers may well have sold him glass imitations for real gem stones. Elizabeth I, his successor to the throne, was equally fond of jewels, and many of her portraits reveal her robes and person to be covered with hundreds of gems and pearls.

Rings had many diverse functions, especially among the medieval clergy, while the gem stones set in them were believed to have symbolic influence. Thus, the blue sapphire stood for purity; the purple amethyst was associated with sobriety; while the grass-green emerald signified tranquillity, happiness, and immortality. Cardinals of the Roman Catholic Church traditionally wear the blue sapphire as a ring stone. Marriage and engagement rings also stem from those early times, and their meaning has changed little through the centuries to the present day.

This was also the time of so-called poison rings, possessing small, concealed containers for poison. Not all such rings had sinister functions, however, for some were used to carry cosmetics and mementos. From the fifteenth century, merchants'-mark rings played an important part in commerce. Made in bronze, brass, and certain gem minerals, they were engraved with selected marks and initials and used by merchants—many of whom were illiterate—to seal contracts and documents.

Certainly, throughout history, gems and jewelry have been acknowledged as status symbols, perhaps one of the most important of the many roles they have played. This may be regarded as a dubious role, for gems certainly have given rise to jealousy and strife among all classes, and perhaps have been in part responsible for many wars fought for no other reason than to win the riches of other nations. But, one must not be unfair to gems, for human nature seems to decree that almost everything judged to be of significant value inevitably arouses some of these unpleasant instincts. If a balance sheet were drawn up, setting the joy and pleasure gems have given to humanity against their less favorable aspects, the credits would definitely outnumber the debits.

One diamond necklace may certainly have influenced the course of history. A magnificent necklace was made to order for the French king, Louis XV, for his mistress, Madame Du Barry. The world was searched to find the most perfect diamonds, for this necklace, with its 647 gems, was to be the greatest gem masterpiece. However, before it could be completed, the king died. For nearly ten years the jewelers tried to sell it to his successor, Louis XVI, and his wife, Marie Antoinette, but neither would purchase the necklace, simply because the price was too high. Eventually, a sinister and cunning plot to steal the piece was devised by a Madame de La Motte. She approached the Cardinal de Rohan, who at this time was out of favor at the French court, and persuaded him to believe that Marie Antoinette wished to purchase the necklace secretly. The cardinal arranged with the jewelers for its purchase. Without having paid for it, he handed the necklace over to Madame de La Motte, who promptly took it to England, where it was broken up and the diamonds sold separately.

The scandal and trials that followed the disappearance of the notorious jewelry rocked the throne of France, and although Louis XVI and Marie Antoinette were innocent parties to the whole affair, which took place in 1786, the suspicion remained in the minds of many people that the queen had secretly tried to acquire the necklace. This, and the extreme extravagance of the French court at this period, may well have hastened the outbreak of the French Revolution and the subsequent executions of Louis and Marie Antoinette.

All this is past history. Today, the role of gems and jewelry in the affairs of state is largely symbolic. Although more and more gem stones are cut and marketed in the world now than at any other period of history, their role has become largely commercial, and possession of them signifies little more than the fact that one owns one of many kinds of property.

Since, as has been shown, the story of gems is inextricably woven with that of jewels, it may be useful to understand more about the jeweler's craft. It will be interesting to see what sort of activities take place at a jewelry maker's.

Modern Jewelry Making

The room is amply provided with large windows. Seated at desks are overalled members of the staff, whose job it is to grade with great care all the gem stones sent to the firm, which will be set in jewelry in the production department. Some of the larger, more valuable stones are meticulously catalogued in a file.

There are many cabinets containing shallow drawers, each subdivided into a number of smaller compartments. These are filled with rubies, sapphires, emeralds, and many other gems. They are skillfully sorted according to size, shape, and quality, so that when a gem of a certain shape or size is required for a piece of jewelry, such a stone can quickly be found. Diamonds are graded for quality, shape, and size and mounted on rectangular pieces of white cardboard over which have been stretched pieces of transparent cellophane to hold them in place.

The design department makes exact drawings and designs of each piece of jewelry before it is assembled. In a brightly lit room, the craftsmen work separately at drawing boards. One artist may be engaged in creating a pair of diamond-and-sapphire earrings, while another may be drawing the design of a fox head, which will later become a brooch, with two red eyes made from rubies. Yet a third works on a model for a diamond necklace that has to be copied from an old photograph taken in the early part of the century. A portion of the picture has been much enlarged, but, even so, it is extremely difficult to recognize details.

Other craftsmen are busy molding designs and drawings into life-size wax and plaster-of-Paris models. These are subsequently painted with the appropriate colors of the gems to be used in their making, so that the designer can see a true replica of the piece before actual work in metal and gems is commenced.

Once drawings and models have been completed, they are sent to the workshops. Here, the real task of shaping and assembling the jewelry begins. Each worker is surrounded by a multitude of specialized files, punches, hammers, and pliers. Numerous electric hand drills hang from the ceiling, each placed in a convenient position so as to be readily available for use. The work benches are also fitted with oxyacetylene burners to enable the craftsmen to soften the precious metals.

Most fine jewelry is handmade, and there are no standard sets of tools available for the work. The craftsmen prefer using their own specialized instruments, most of which they have made themselves. Sometimes a worn file that has been shaped and turned correctly may become the craftsman's most treasured device. With infinite care, a man will hammer into shape tiny gold leaves that are to form part of a brooch. Another shapes the

Yellow Sapphire	Ruby	Golden Sapphire	Blue Sapphire	Pink Sapphire
Green Beryl	Aquamarine	Yellow Beryl	Pink Beryl	Emerald
Chrysoberyl	Alexandrite*	Sherry-colored Topaz	Blue Topaz	Pink Topaz
Peridot	Citrine	Amethyst	Green Tourmaline	Red Tourmaline

** The brownish color of the Alexandrite is due to photographic floodlighting. The stone appeared green in daylight*

setting out of a piece of platinum for a large diamond. Yet another carefully measures the size of an emerald that is to form the centerpiece of a ring.

Although the jewelry is designed on paper and a wax model of it is made for the guidance of the craftsman concerned, much of the beauty of the final product will depend upon his own originality and skill. Broadly speaking, the methods used to fashion the best of modern jewelry have changed little over the centuries, and when one watches these men at work, one leaves behind the hustle and bustle of the twentieth century and enters a world where speed means little, but pride in workmanship is in full accord with ancient tradition.

This is the way the best jewelry, much of which is still specially commissioned, is produced. It must not be overlooked, however, that the industrialization of the twentieth century has also had its impact on the craft of jewelry making. Much of the work on precious metals, hitherto the sole prerogative of the goldsmith, is today carried out by modern machinery. The melting of gold bars and the drawing of wire is no longer carried out by the craftsmen themselves. Large refining firms undertake this project, and ready-made gold sheets and wire made from the precious metals can now be purchased in required shapes and sizes. The making of bracelets, too, has been partially mechanized, and machines can now produce long lengths of different chain designs quickly and relatively cheaply. A mechanized method of engraving metals, known as *engine turning,* and the technique of *centrifugal casting,* have all helped to make jewelry more readily available at prices within the means of most people today.

Although fashion in jewelry changes like fashion in all other forms of art, it can, in some ways, be likened to the changing tastes in music. For instance, a Beethoven symphony composed in the nineteenth century has lost nothing in dignity and beauty during the course of time, though music has changed considerably over the years. In the same way, jewelry created in the sixteenth century by Cellini is as precious and beautiful today as it was then.

Today, modern artists and sculptors are making valuable contributions that often closely follow the lines of their work with the paint brush and the chisel. The beauty of uncut gem crystals has been rediscovered, and

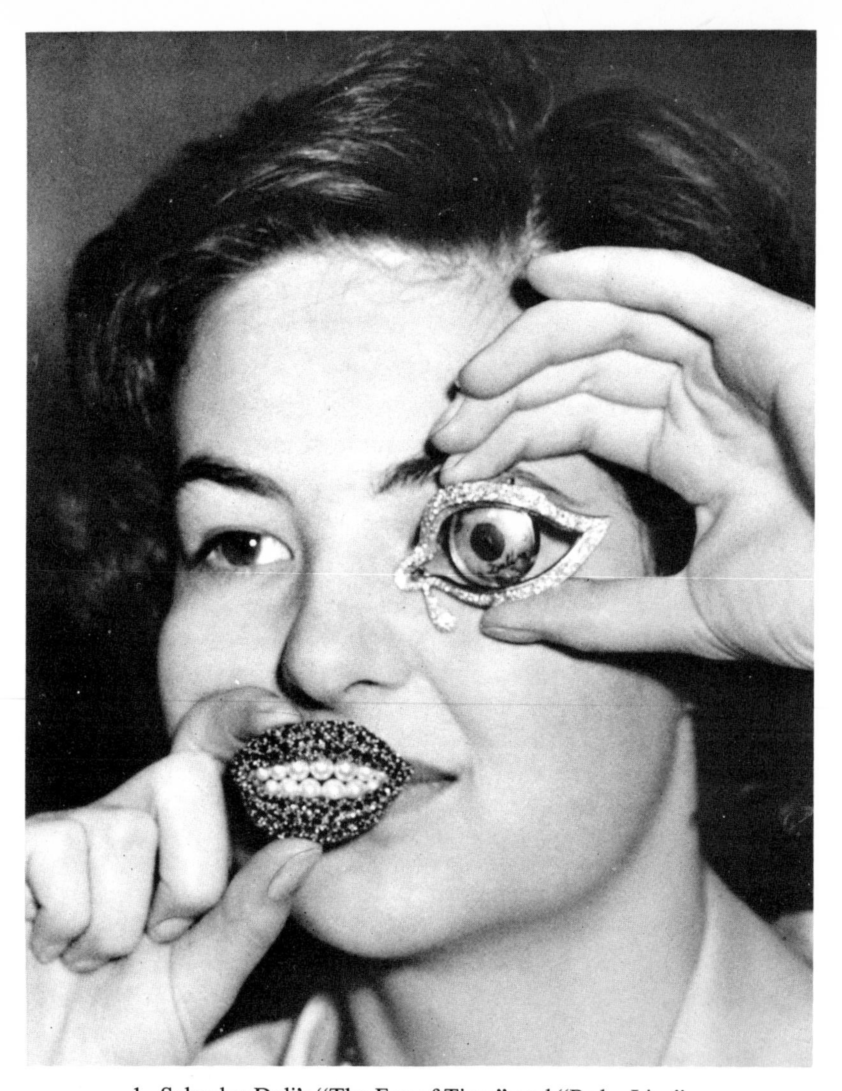

1. Salvador Dali's "The Eye of Time" and "Ruby Lips"

stones carefully selected for their shape and natural impurities are increasingly incorporated in designs of contemporary artist-craftsmen. Often, quite common and inexpensive minerals—such as rock crystal, rose quartz, or iron pyrites—when set in their natural forms in artistically designed gold mounts make exceedingly attractive brooches and rings.

Creations by the well-known Spanish surrealist painter, Salvador Dali, a master of modern jewelry creation, are splendid examples of how the designs of his art can be realized in precious metal and gems. One of his pieces is a golden heart with a jeweled crown, within which there is an animated, pulsating heart. The jewel, Dali says, signifies the ruler whose heart beats for her people. While this may not be everyone's idea of a pleasant piece of jewelry, it is certainly startling. All departures from the conventional meet with criticism, yet, as the years pass, they become commonplace. Dali's creations include a pair of telephone ear clips, made of precious stones, a pair of ruby lips, the rubies being set individually in gold with pearls, and a watch, called "The Eye of Time." The watch, in three shades of blue enamel, is set in a diamond clip shaped like the human eye. Some of his designs are not meant to be worn because of their enormous size; the largest measures about 10 by 30 inches. All of them, however, show a burst of great creative genius that, together with the very nature of the fine material he uses, insure that they become splendid objects of decorative beauty.

II

THE NATURE OF GEMS

Origin and Composition

Natural gems are derived from the three kingdoms of nature: animal, vegetable, and mineral. To the first two belong all things that are living or have lived. These are called *organic;* examples of organic substances are rubber, wood, ivory, and pearl. The substances of the mineral kingdom consist of matter that has never lived, such as common salt, gold, and iron. These are called *inorganic.* Only a few gems, for example, pearls and amber, are organic in origin. The vast majority are inorganic and come from the mineral kingdom.

The earth is composed of many different kinds of rock, and if a hole were to be drilled from the North Pole to its center, it would require a drill 3,950 miles long. Nobody has so far been able to drill deeper into the earth than about 4¾ miles, and therefore our knowledge of the mineral kingdom is confined to a very thin layer of the earth's crust. Each of the many different kinds of rock that make up this crust is composed of individual substances called *minerals.* An example of a common mineral is salt. There are many others, some extremely hard—diamond, for example—while others, such as asbestos, are comparatively soft. Some may be beautifully colored, while others are of indifferent shades. The most sought-after minerals for gem stones are those that are hard and tough, yet have an attractive appearance.

All minerals are composed of one or more *elements*. An element is a substance that cannot be split up into any other ones by chemical means. Gold and oxygen are examples of elements. The vast numbers of substances on earth, whether they are organic or inorganic in origin, are composed of elements. In fact, only 89 elements are found in nature. It is from these 89 elements that all other substances are formed by joining the elements together in vastly differing combinations and quantities.

To each of the elements has been allotted a special symbol by which they are internationally known. For example: aluminum is represented by the symbol "Al," and oxygen by the symbol "O." Some other important elements are barium (Ba), beryllium (Be), bromine (Br), calcium (Ca), carbon (C), chlorine (Cl), cobalt (Co), copper (Cu), chromium (Cr), fluorine (F), gold (Au), hydrogen (H), iodine (I), iron (Fe), lead (Pb), magnesium (Mg), mercury (Hg), nitrogen (N), potassium (K), silicon (Si), silver (Ag), sodium (Na) and zinc (Zn).

Of all gem stones, the diamond alone consists of but a single element, carbon—the same carbon that comes down chimneys as soot or, as graphite, is used in pencils; all the others are *compounds*, made up of two or more elements joined together.

An example of a gem stone made of two elements is the ruby. It consists of aluminum and oxygen—the same aluminum from which the saucepans in the kitchen are made and the same oxygen that is in the air all around us and without which we could not breathe. The compound is called aluminum oxide, and it is represented by the symbols Al_2O_3.

One might ask how it is that carbon can compose the diamond, and yet at the same time can also be soot or graphite. To answer this question it is necessary to delve deeper into the mysteries of nature and find out what an element is made of. All elements and compounds, including gems, are composed of *atoms;* each element is composed of only one type of atom.

Suppose a bar of gold is cut into smaller and smaller pieces. First the bar would be cut in half, then one of the halves would itself be halved. Then one of the quarters thus obtained would be halved, and this halving process would be continued millions of times until at last an extremely tiny piece of gold would be obtained that would be the smallest piece of substance still possessing the properties of gold. To this final and chemically indivisible piece, the name *atom* has been given. Only a few of them can exist on their own; most must join together with others to form what are called *molecules,* the smallest particles of an element or compound that can normally exist. Thus, for example, oxygen in the air does not consist of a collection of independent oxygen atoms. It is known that the oxygen atoms unite in pairs to form molecules.

To return to the symbols for each element, each symbol represents one individual atom of an element. Thus O represents an atom of oxygen and O_2 represents a molecule of oxygen, which consists of two oxygen atoms joined together. Two separate oxygen molecules are represented by $2O_2$. It should, therefore, be clear what the ruby is made of when its formula is written Al_2O_3. One molecule of the gem consists of two aluminum atoms and three oxygen atoms in combination. This is called its chemical composition. There is also a minute amount of another element present, which gives it its beautiful red color, but for the time being this will be ignored. The number of atoms in a molecule vary from two, as in oxygen, to many hundreds, as in some organic compounds. Chemical composition is important when determining the identity of a mineral. There is, however, another equally important factor.

The Mineral Crystals

In a *crystal,* the atoms are arranged in a definite and repetitive pattern. That means each piece of crystal consists of a definite number of atoms of the component elements arranged in a precise pattern. The result of this regular atomic arrangement is that crystals show definite external geometrical shapes, bounded by plane faces. An example is the mineral quartz found in many parts of the world (see Fig. 2).

Most minerals occur in nature in crystalline form; thus their appearance

2. Large crystal of quartz

and many of their properties largely depend upon the arrangement of the atoms within them. We call this their *crystalline structure.*

It has already been mentioned that carbon can exist in the beautiful form of the diamond, but that it also occurs as graphite and soot. The fact is that one chemical substance can have two or three completely different appearances; this does not apply only to the element carbon, but to many other substances.

If Fig. 4, showing the atomic arrangement of the diamond crystal, is compared with Fig. 3, showing the atomic arrangement of graphite—which also has a crystalline structure—it is found that in the diamond crystal the carbon atoms are held together by strong bonds and form a solid pyramid, which explains the diamond's extreme hardness and resistance to external influences. In the graphite crystal, however, the atoms are arranged in flat, six-sided sheets, and these sheets are themselves only loosely linked with

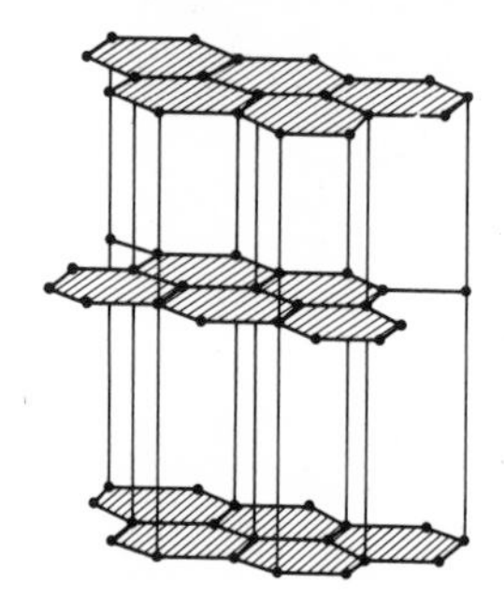

3. Arrangement of carbon atoms in graphite

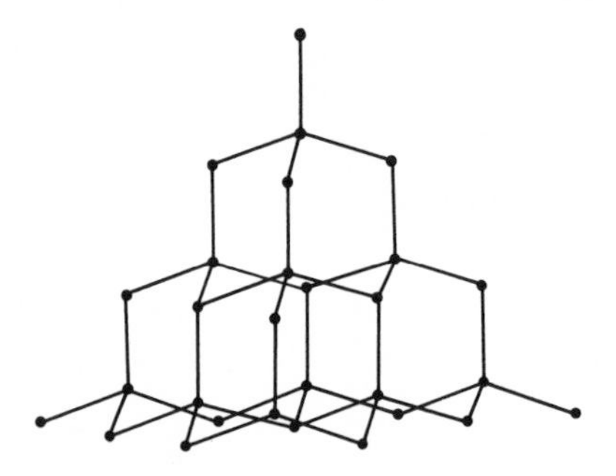

4. Arrangement of carbon atoms in a diamond crystal

one another. This means that they can slide over each other. Thus, graphite is greasy to the touch and can be used as a lubricant when mixed with grease.

In nature, some gem minerals are found in the form of regular and symmetrical crystals with natural, lustrous plane faces. Some are indeed so perfect that they are used for native jewelry without being cut or polished. An example is the spinel crystal (see Color Plate II).

It must not, however, be assumed that a mineral can occur in any crystal shape. This is not so. To begin with, each mineral that occurs in crystalline form belongs to one of seven systems, and when the crystal system of a gem mineral in its natural form can be recognized, a great deal can be learned about that mineral's identity. For example, if some natural diamond crystals are examined, it is found that this mineral normally crystallizes in the shape of a double pyramid called an *octahedron* (see Fig. 5). Thus we know that

5. Some forms of the cubic crystal system (*a*) Cube (6-sided) (*b*) Octahedron (8-sided) (*c*) Dodecahedron (12-sided)

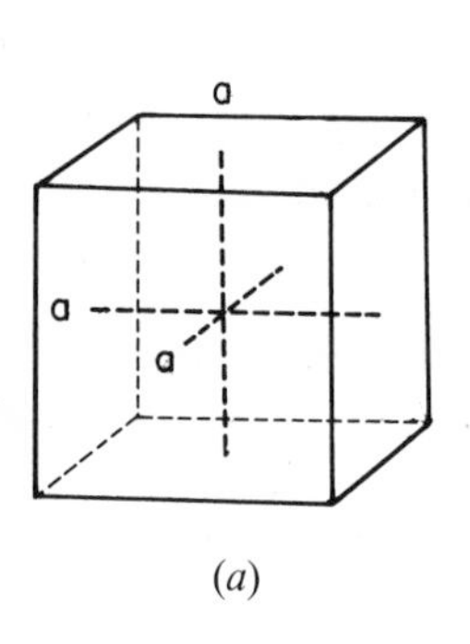

(*a*)

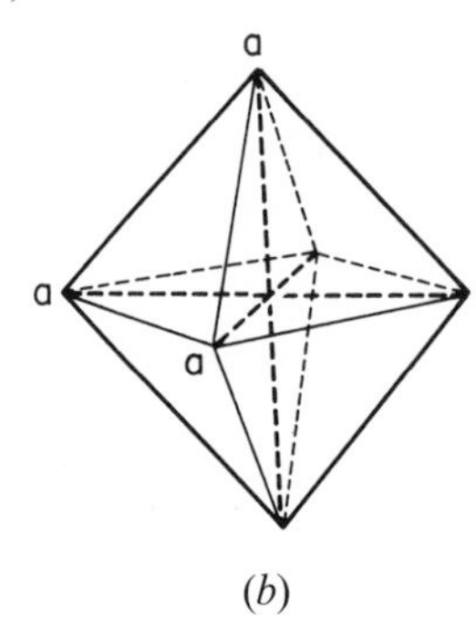

(*b*)

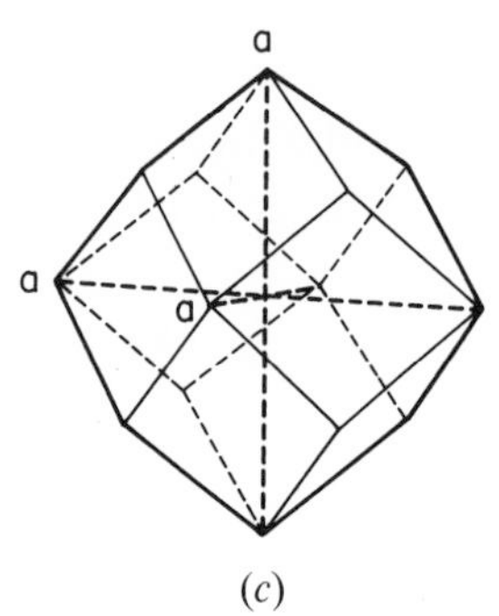

(*c*)

6. Large natural crystals of rock salt, showing their cubic crystal shape

a crystal of this shape can belong only to the so-called cubic crystal system, and therefore it can be deduced immediately that the mineral must belong to that system.

In order to define a crystal system, certain imaginary lines of reference must exist in order to describe the relative positions of the crystal faces. These imaginary lines are called *crystal axes* and there are usually three, or at the most four, such axes, which all intersect in the crystal's center. The important thing to remember is that in each crystal system the crystal axes are arranged in one particular, fixed way that never varies, whatever form the crystal may take.

Perhaps the simplest of all crystal systems is the *cubic* one where the three crystal axes are all of an equal length, and intersect one another at right angles. Figure 5 illustrates the crystal shapes of the cube, the octahedron, and the *dodecahedron,* all of which belong to the cubic system and can therefore be described by the same three crystal axes (*a*). The diamond is usually

7. Diamond crystal in blue ground with loose diamond crystals showing their octahedral habit

found in the form of an octahedron and thus is described as being of octahedral habit.

The gem stone zircon occurs in crystals of the *tetragonal* system. As Fig. 8 shows, these crystals look rather like building bricks. They have three crystal axes that intersect one another at right angles, but, unlike the cubic system, only two of these crystal axes (*a*) are of equal length, and the third vertical axis (*c*) is unequal.

In nature, crystals of the emerald occur like regular six-sided pillars (see Fig. 10), and these belong to what is known as the *hexagonal* crystal system. This is one of two systems that have four crystal axes. Three of these axes (*a*) are of equal length and cross one another at angles of 60°, while the fourth axis (*c*) is unequal and stands at right angles to the plane formed by the other three.

8. The tetragonal crystal system

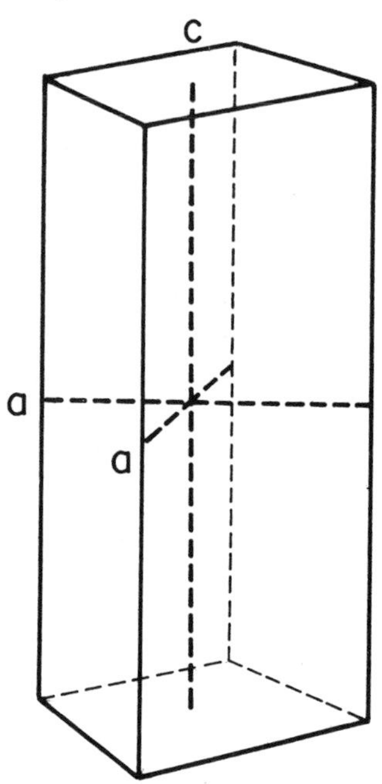

9. Large zircon crystal showing its tetragonal crystal system

Similarly, the remaining four crystal systems are described by their respective crystal axes. The *triclinic* system (see Fig. 11) has three crystal axes, unequal in length and intersecting obliquely: *c* is the vertical axis; *a* is the shorter horizontal axis running from back to front, also known as "brachyaxis" (*brachy* in Greek means short); *b* is the longer horizontal axis running from right to left, also known as "macroaxis" (*macro* in Greek means long). The *orthorhombic* crystal system has three crystal axes (*a*, *b*, *c*), unequal in length and at right angles to each other (see Fig. 12). The *monoclinic* crystal system has three unequal crystal axes (*a*, *b*, *c*), one at right angles to the other two, which intersect obliquely (see Fig. 13).

One fascinating aspect of crystals is that they exhibit what are called directional properties. This rather grand-sounding phrase is best explained by some practical examples. A ruby crystal may, for instance, have a good red color if viewed from one direction, yet from another it will look brownish red. The explanation, of course, lies with the atomic patterns within the crystal itself, which allow certain colors to pass in one direction but not in another.

The diamond, despite its hardness, can be split easily in any plane parallel to a crystal face of the octahedron. This is comparable to a man chopping firewood. It is far more difficult to split a log across the grain of the wood

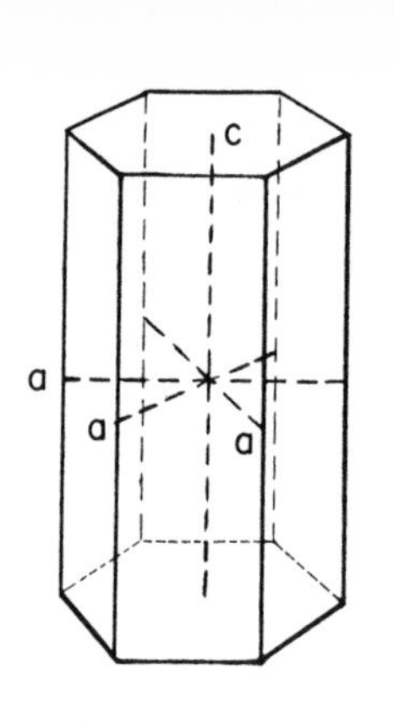

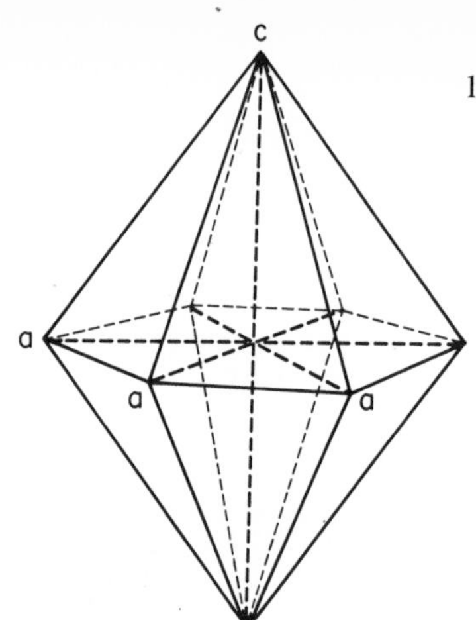

10. The hexagonal crystal system; (Left) a hexagonal prism; (Right) a hexagonal bipyramid

11. The triclinic crystal system

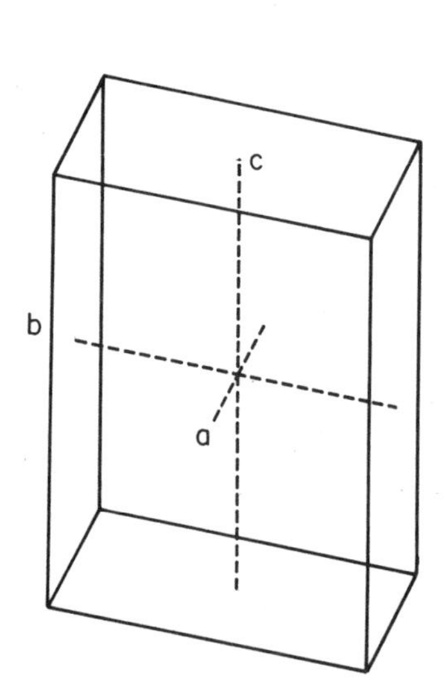

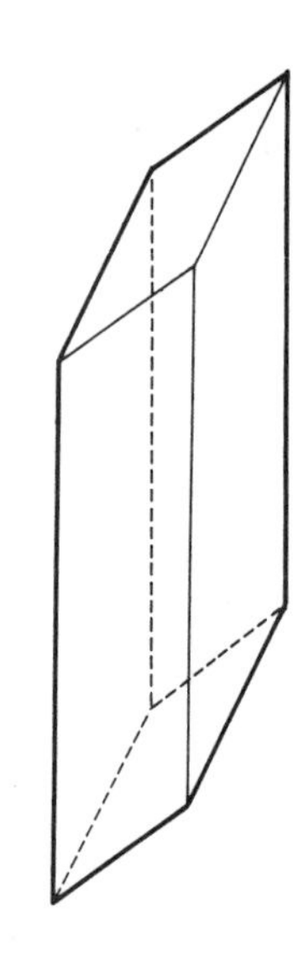

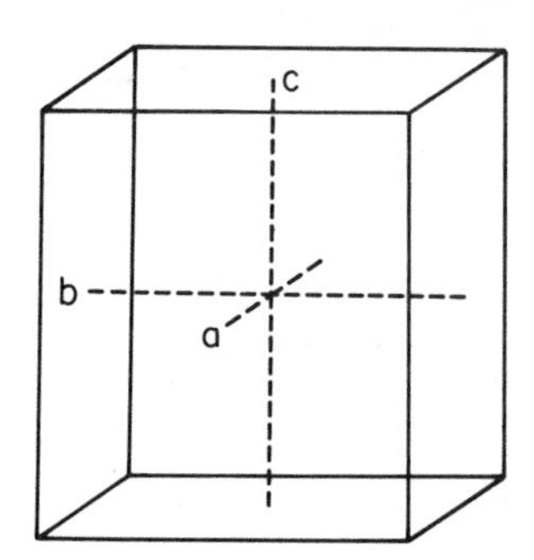

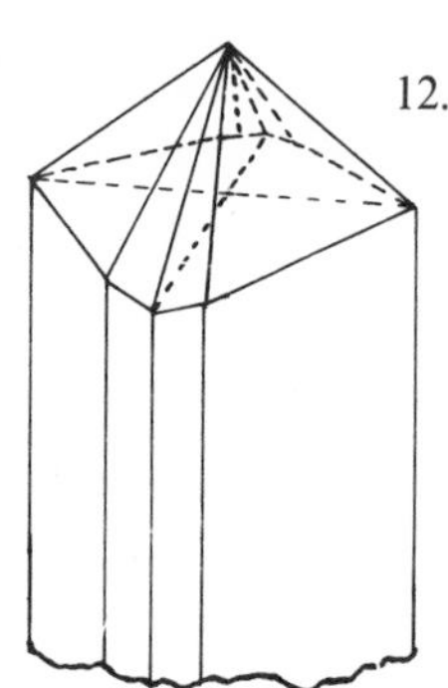

12. The orthorhombic crystal system

13. The monoclinic crystal system

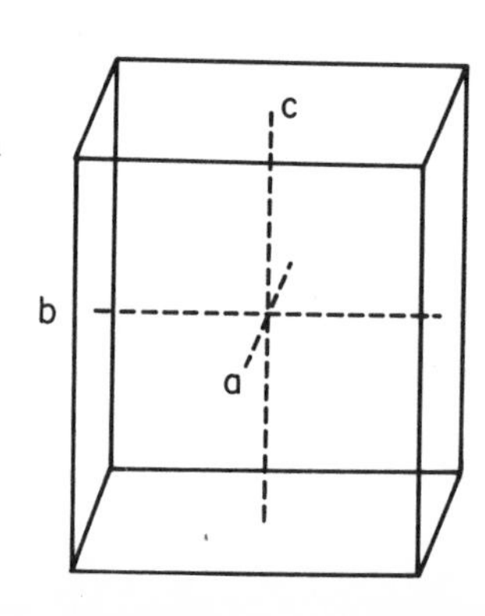

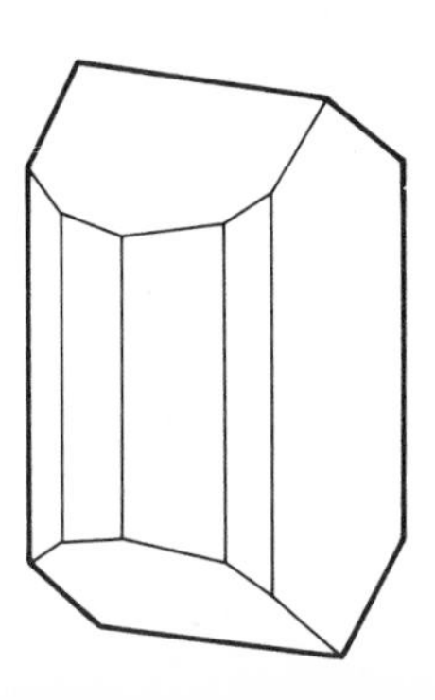

fibers than it is to do so lengthwise in the direction of the fibers. The reason is that the wood fibers are extremely tough and difficult to cut across, whereas the individual fibers are only relatively loosely joined together. Similarly, there are certain directions in a diamond crystal where the atoms are linked more loosely, and in these directions it is possible to split a diamond without great difficulty. In any other direction, the atoms hold tightly together and cannot be parted.

These directional properties must receive careful consideration when crystals are chosen for gem stones, and the beauty of the final product will depend upon the skill and knowledge of the *lapidarist,* or gem cutter whose job it is to cut and polish them.

The Mystery of Light

The beauty of gems is conveyed to us through our eyes, by the medium of light. Without light, however, the sparkling diamond loses its luster and the ruby its fine red color. Without light, the world would be pitch black, and no one would ever be aware of the beauty of gem stones.

Almost from the dawn of civilization, this phenomenon of light and the way it reflects and projects has intrigued and puzzled scientists, and many conflicting theories have been formulated about its real nature. None of them fully explain this phenomenon, but the most convenient explanation is *the wave,* or *undulatory, theory.* According to this, light consists of electromagnetic waves that emanate in all directions in straight lines from a luminous source, such as the sun or an electric light bulb. One of the most puzzling features of light is its incredible speed. It takes only about 8 minutes for sunlight to reach the earth, and it has been calculated that light travels through outer space at the phenomenal speed of about 186,000 miles per second. The most modern rockets and man-made satellites rarely exceed a speed of 20,000 miles per hour.

The famous English scientist, Sir Isaac Newton (1642–1727), made a fundamental discovery when he passed a narrow beam of white sunlight through a glass prism (see Fig. 14). He found that a beam of ordinary white light splits up into a colored band similar to that of the rainbow. Since then, it has become common practice to speak of white light as being composed of

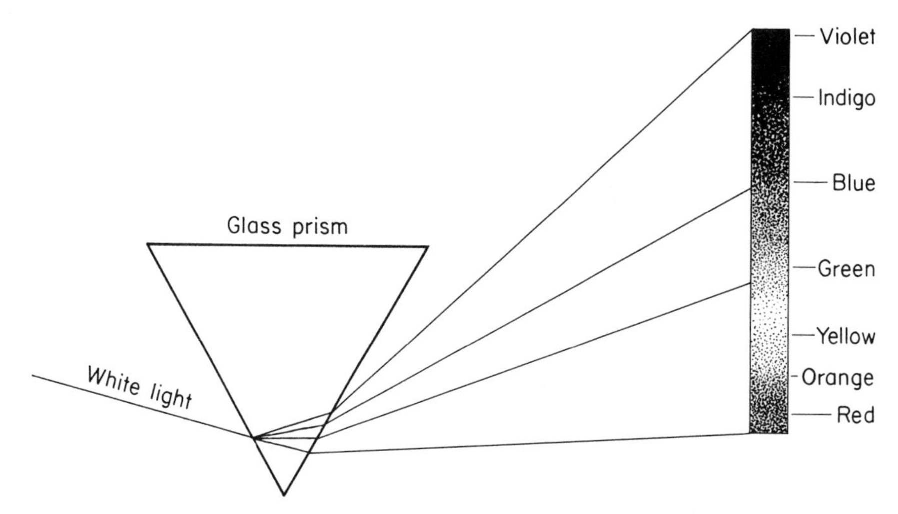

14. Dispersion of light

seven principal colors—red, orange, yellow, green, blue, indigo, and violet. This is also called the *solar,* or *visible, spectrum,* and each of these colors gradually merges into the next one. This splitting up of light into its spectrum colors is known as *dispersion* and also occurs when light enters gem stones. The amount of dispersion a gem can produce determines its so-called fire—a characteristic of the utmost importance in colorless, transparent gem stones, for without this fire they would look dull and uninteresting. The sparkle of the diamond is due almost entirely to its great fire.

Each shade of the spectrum is produced by light waves of a fixed and definite wave length, and the colors seen in everyday life are usually a mixture of several spectrum colors in varying proportions. Light waves are extremely short, so short in fact that a special unit, the *Ångström,* had to be devised to measure them. An Ångström unit, represented by the symbol Å, is only 1/10,000,000 millimeter in length. The longest light waves produce red light, whose wave lengths may vary between 7,500 Å and 6,500 Å. The shortest light waves produce violet light and its wave length hovers between 4,000 Å and 3,900 Å. Figure 15 shows diagrammatically a violet and a red wave length. The wave lengths of visible light range from about 7,500 Å, in the red part of the spectrum, to 3,900 Å, in the violet part of the spectrum. Beyond 7,500 Å lie the still longer, and invisible, infrared and radio waves, and beyond the violet end of the spectrum lie the shorter, and invisible, ultraviolet rays, x-rays, gamma rays, and cosmic rays.

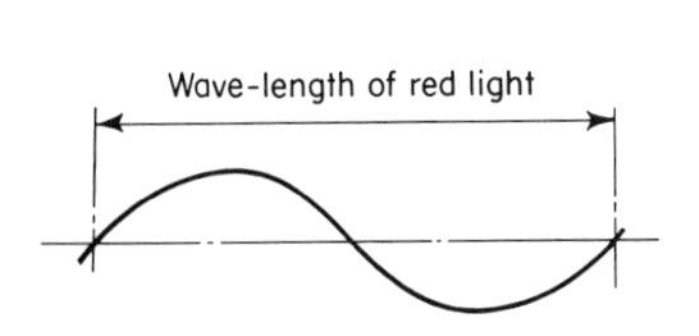

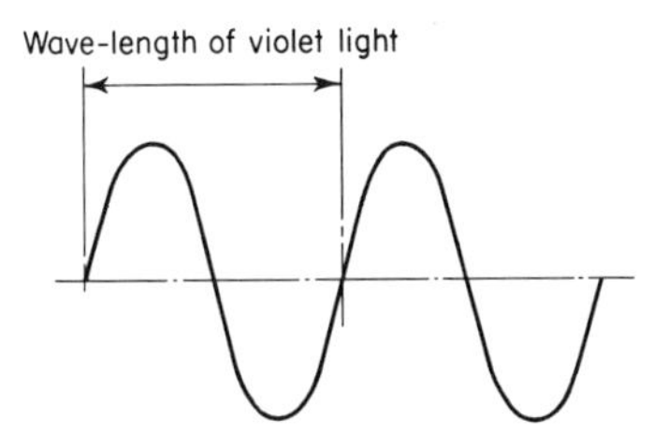

15. The nature of light

Let us take a closer look at the way light behaves by studying a ray of sunlight that falls upon an ordinary glass mirror. A mirror will reflect light, which always observes certain strict laws that govern its mode of travel. Take, for example, the mirror in Fig. 16. *AO* is a ray of light falling obliquely upon the mirror surface at *O*. The ray is turned back or *reflected* from the mirror surface along *OR*. Imagine *OB* to be a line drawn perpendicular, or *normal,* to the surface of the mirror at *O*. The interesting thing is that the angle of incidence, *AOB,* at which the light strikes the mirror, is always equal to the angle of reflection, *BOR;* also, the incident ray, *AO,* the reflected ray, *OR,* and the normal, *OB,* lie all in one plane.

These are the laws of reflection and are observable often in daily life, for instance, the spot of light that appears on the ceiling of the living room when a ray of sunlight from the window is reflected from the surface of a cup of tea. The effects of light reflection are also of great importance in cut gem stones, and they play a large part in their lustrous and brilliant appearance.

Yet another phenomenon, which is called *refraction,* also plays an important part in the appearance of gems. Imagine that a ray of light strikes the surface of a transparent gem stone; this is illustrated in Fig. 17. It can rightly be assumed that if a ray of light, *AO,* impinges on the surface of a transparent gem stone, part of the light will continue through the stone, but instead of passing on in a straight line, the direction of the light changes, and it will travel in a direction similar to *OR*. This bending of the ray is called refraction, and when light is passing from a rarer medium, such as air, to a denser medium, such as a gem stone, the refracted ray, *OR*, is bent toward the normal, *BON*. The incident ray, the normal, and the refracted ray are all in one plane. But if it travels the other way from the denser to the rarer medium, that is, from the gem stone into air, the ray will be refracted from the normal, *BON*, along a path similar to *OA*, as shown in Fig. 18.

One more peculiar property of mineral crystals is their ability to split light rays in two. All mineral crystals can do this with the exception of those, such as the diamond, belonging to the cubic system. This phenomenon is called *double refraction* (see Fig. 19), and if light enters such a mineral crystal, the light rays are not only bent, but they are also split, generally into two refracted rays, which will take different paths. In the drawing, *AO* represents the incident ray, *OR* and *OR′* are the two refracted rays. *BN* is the normal. This ability to split light is demonstrated in Fig. 20 by a large crystal of Iceland spar, one of the strongest doubly refractive minerals known. Many gem stones exhibit this property, and, in some cases, it forms a useful key to their identification.

It is obvious that the subject of light is also closely connected with the color of gems, and it is not an unreasonable question to ask why the ruby looks red.

The answer to this question is *color absorption.* Different substances have the power to absorb different wave lengths of light, and the ultimate color of a gem or any other material will depend on the kinds and amounts of wave lengths that are not absorbed by the substance. In the ruby certain chemical substances are present that will absorb all wave lengths of light except those that look red to our eyes. As a result, the ruby looks red. Even a colorless, transparent stone, such as the diamond, will absorb a little light, but all wave lengths will be absorbed in the same proportion, and it will therefore remain colorless.

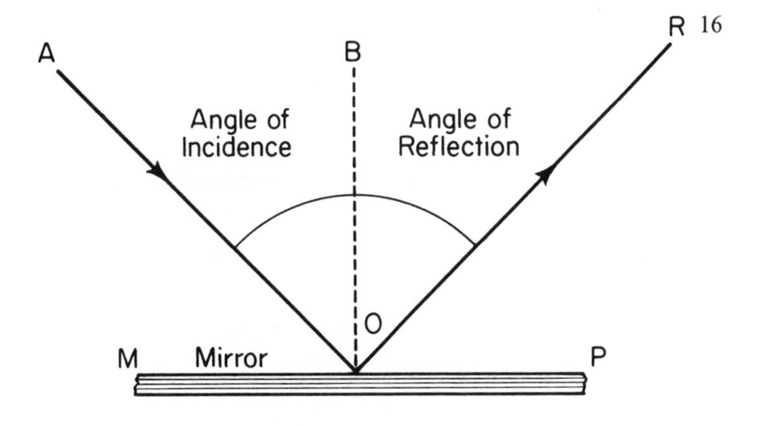

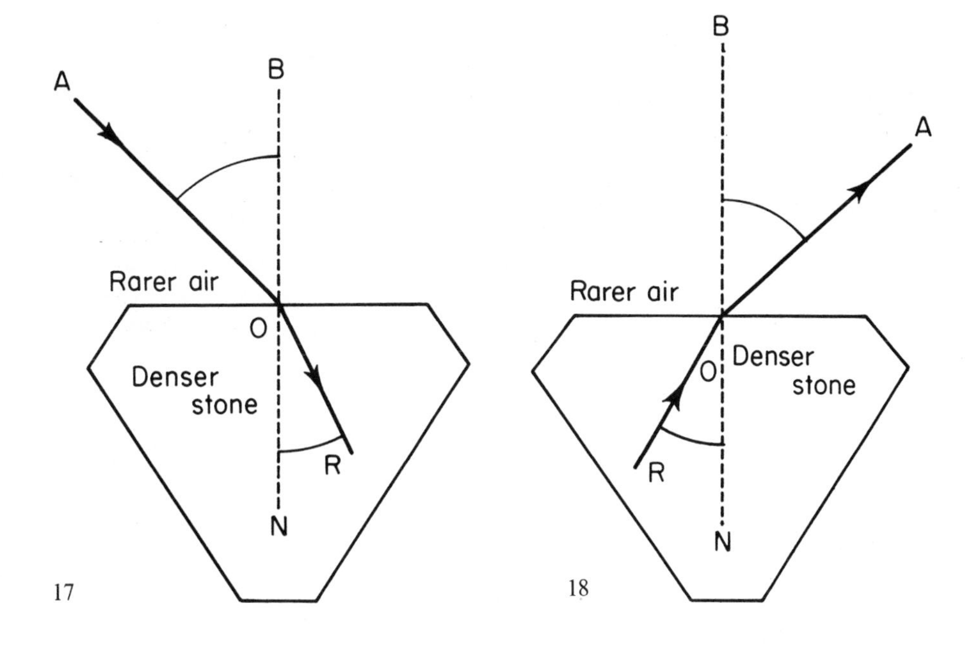

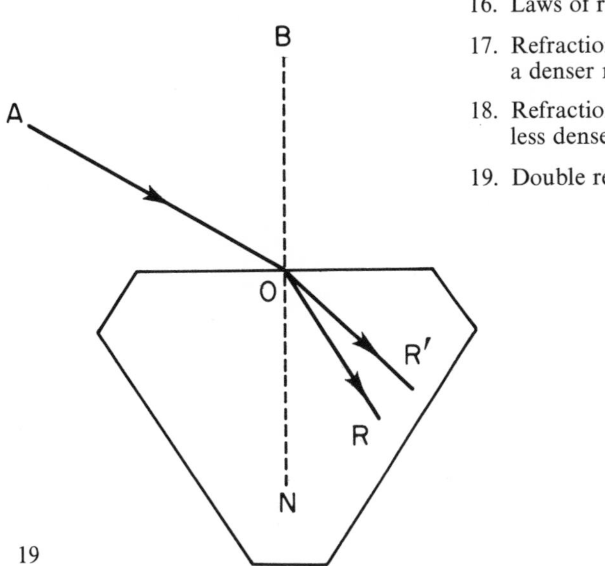

16. Laws of reflection
17. Refraction from a less dense to a denser medium
18. Refraction from a denser to a less dense medium
19. Double refraction

The Hardness of Gem Stones

The hardness of almost any material is of considerable importance when it has to stand up to a great deal of wear and tear. This toughness is considered to be of special importance with regard to gem minerals, since not only should they be able to stand up to a considerable amount of wear, often through decades or even centuries, but they must also be durable and able to withstand millions of years of harsh treatment by nature while they are still being washed about in rivers, streams, or crushed by mountains long before we find them and make them into gems.

The *hardness* of a gem stone may best be defined as the amount of resistance its surface sets up when an attempt is made to scratch it with another stone or object. Diamonds are sometimes used to cut window glass. In the same way, an emerald can be scratched with a ruby, but not the other way around, because the latter is harder than the former.

In order to simplify the method of expressing the various degrees of hardness, a German physicist, Friedrich Mohs (1773–1839), devised an arbitrary scale of hardness. He took ten minerals and arranged them in the order of their respective hardnesses. Thus, diamond was placed at the top of the scale, with its hardness assigned as number 10. The ruby came next, with hard-

20. Iceland spar showing strong double refraction

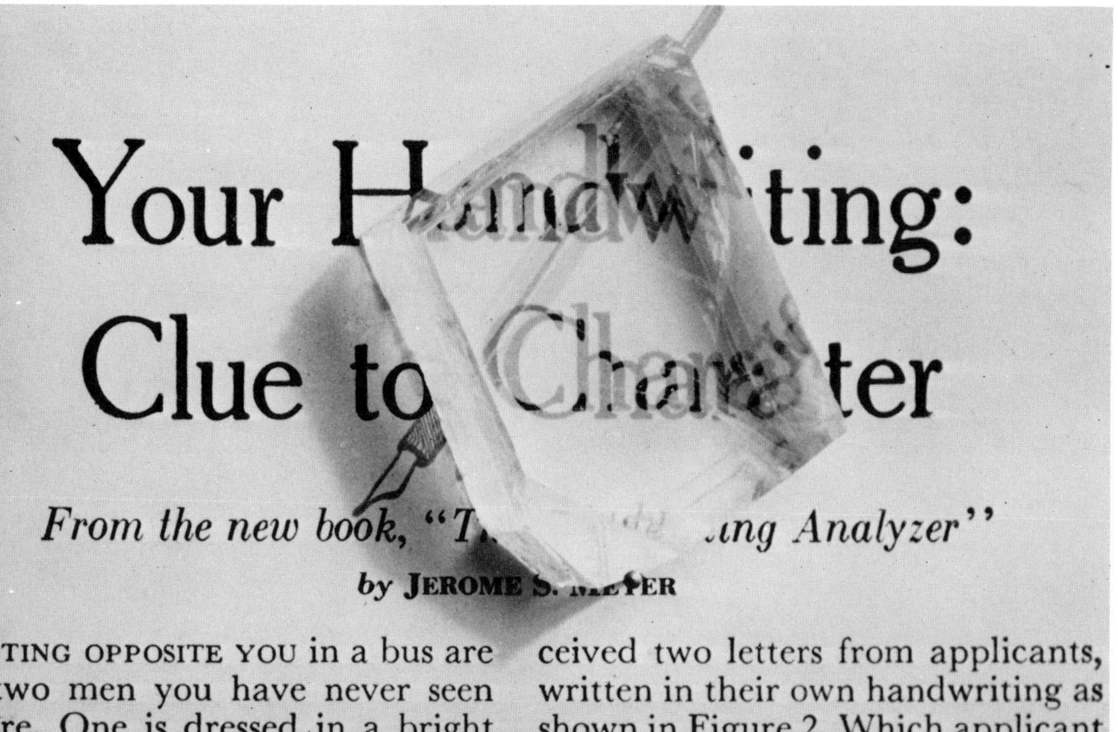

ness 9; then followed the topaz, with hardness 8; and quartz, with hardness 7; feldspar, 6; apatite, 5; fluorite, 4; calcite, 3; gypsum, 2; talc, 1.

The numbers in the hardness scale are only an indication of the order of hardness and have no other significance. Thus, the hardness interval between diamond and ruby is far greater than that between ruby and topaz. This simply means that the ruby is the next hardest natural substance on earth after the diamond; however, the hardness interval between those first two is so great that it exceeds that between ruby (hardness 9) and talc (hardness 1).

Testing the identity of stones simply by scratching one with another may seem at first to be a simple and quick method, but such tests are not really permissible. If you possessed an emerald ring and someone tested it for hardness with a diamond, it might be badly scratched and lose much of its value. For this reason, hardness tests are much frowned upon and should not be used if damage is likely to result.

The surprising thing is that the same mineral crystal may possess a number of different hardnesses. There is, for example, an interesting mineral called cyanite, the crystals of which, in some directions, are soft enough to be scratched with a steel-bladed knife but will resist all attempts in other directions. The reason for this extraordinary behavior can again be traced back to the regular atomic patterns within the crystals, which will resist the steel blade in some directions but not in others, and is one more example of their directional properties.

III  DIAMONDS

The diamond may well be called the king of gems. As the hardest mineral substance known to man, it combines decorative beauty with an ever increasing usefulness in science and technology.

Diamonds occur in nature in various crystal forms but, as was stated earlier, are most commonly found in the shape of the octahedron. Occasionally, crystals are found where each face of the octahedron has been replaced by three smaller faces, so that the crystal becomes twenty-four sided (Fig. 21*a*). There may even be diamond crystals with forty-eight faces (Fig. 21*b*) or twelve faces (Fig. 5*c*), and they can also occur in the shape of the simple six-sided cube.

Diamonds, however, do not only occur in single crystals. In Brazil, particularly, they are sometimes found in lumps comprising many tiny, impure crystals tightly packed together. In this form, they are known as *carbonado,* a substance highly prized for its uses in industry.

The tight atomic arrangement within the diamond crystals makes them

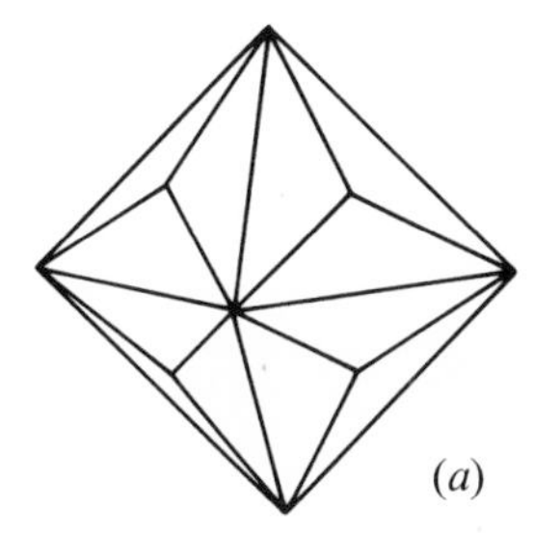
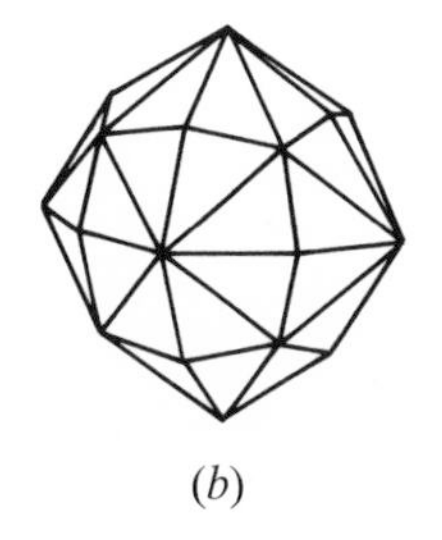
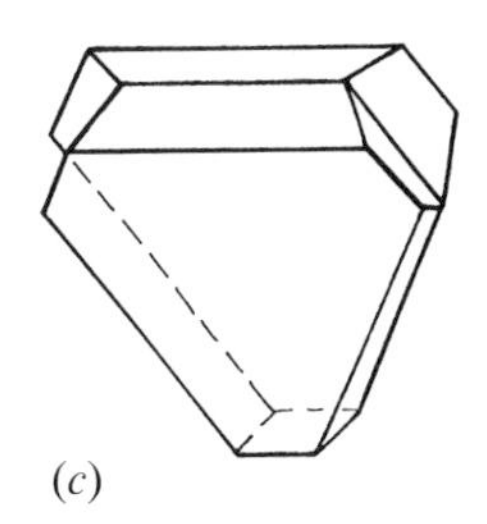

21. Forms in which the diamond can appear (*a*) Trisoctahedron (*b*) Hexoctahedron (*c*) Twinned octahedron

extremely resistant to most external influences. Even the strongest acids have little effect upon them at ordinary temperature. Yet, if heated in air to a temperature of 900° centigrade, a diamond will burn until there is very little of it left, for it will be converted almost completely into the gas carbon dioxide (CO_2) and disappear into the atmosphere.

Diamond material in its many varying shapes and forms is not as rare as is commonly believed. Only in its purest colorless form is it a scarce and valuable gem stone that can be made to reach a final peak of beauty after it has been skillfully cut and polished.

Diamonds are found in India, Brazil, the United States, Australia, the Soviet Union, and in many parts of Africa, where the world's most important deposits are situated. Large diamond fields are located in The Republic of the Congo; as a source of industrial stones these fields form the most important deposits in the world today, providing some 60 per cent of the total world's industrial diamond output. Ghana, too, has rich diamond fields, and even more productive ones have been discovered in Sierra Leone. But by far the richest source of gem diamonds lies in the Republic of South Africa. The diamond-mining industry there is the largest in the world, and South Africa's diamond exports are of major importance to its economy.

The industry began there in the year 1867, when the children of the Boer farmer, Daniel Jacobs of Hopetown, whose land stretched along the banks of the Orange River, picked up a white pebble and began to play with it. The pebble attracted the attention of a neighbor, and, after it had been

22. The old workings at the Premier Mine at Cullinan, Transvaal, a reminder of early days when recovery was by open cast methods. Today, the blue ground is mined underground

examined by several people, it was finally discovered to be a diamond of considerable value.

This accidental discovery was to have a far-reaching influence upon the whole course of South African history. It led to the first "diamond rush" and the so-called river diggings, for the lode of precious diamonds extended to the River Vaal. Prospecting proceeded at a feverish pace. Rivers were diverted into temporary channels and their beds torn up in a frantic search for diamonds. A few lucky men quickly made fortunes, but the majority were less fortunate and barely eked out a living as a reward for their labors. The river diggings were of a type similar to those found in India and Brazil, the diamonds being located in deposits of gravel of limited thickness beneath which was barren rock.

In 1870, more diamonds were discovered in shallow depressions in certain ground on a dry plateau at the farm Jagersfontein, near Fauresmith in the Orange Free State. This led to a further diamond rush and to the founding of the now famous town of Kimberley. The mines there were distinguished as *dry diggings,* and proved to be of an entirely new type. The term was applied to these mines because of their arid surroundings as opposed to the river diggings on the River Vaal.

At first, miners working the surface deposits of the dry diggings thought the yellowish rock underlying them was barren, just as the bed rock of the river gravels had been. Then someone investigated this rock more closely and found to his surprise that it was even richer in diamonds than the surface layer, and, after digging to a depth of some 60 feet, the miners came upon a still harder bluish rock, which they called *blue ground.* This contained a real wealth of diamonds.

The surface area of these dry diggings varies considerably, but the largest of them in the Transvaal, known as the Premier Mine, is oval shaped and measures about 1,000 by 500 yards. There are, of course, many other smaller ones. Their depth seems unlimited. The well-known workings of the Kimberley Mine now extend to a depth of well over 3,000 feet and are still in diamond-bearing ground.

23. Aerial view of the Premier Mine

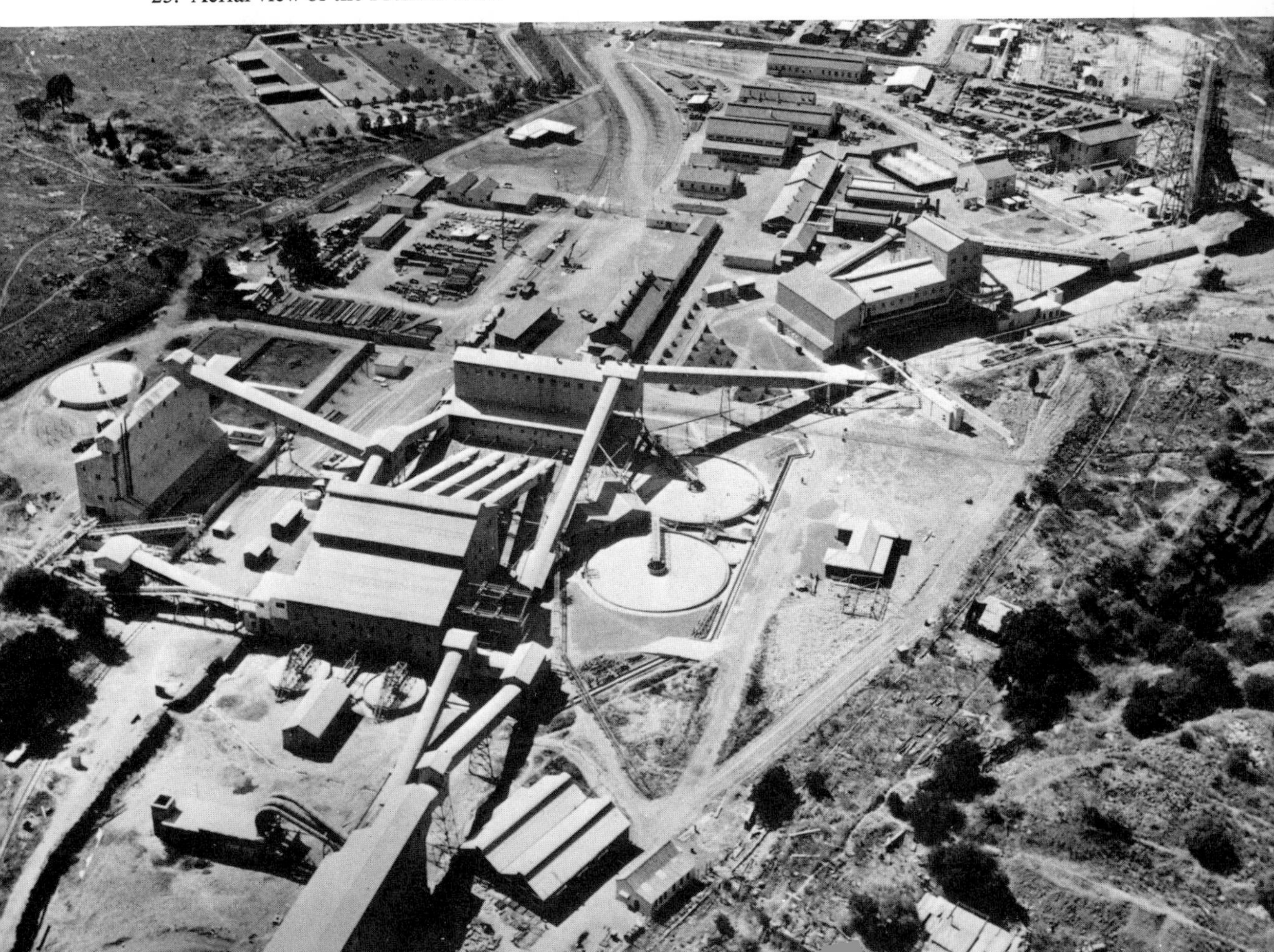

24. This rotary scoop removes 600 tons of sand an hour to expose the diamond-bearing gravels that lie buried beneath 50 feet or more of overburden

It is believed that diamonds were first formed some 60 million years ago and that these huge *pipes* are the necks of ancient volcanoes that may have erupted violently, perhaps under the surface of the earth, bringing up vast masses of materials from the bowels of our planet. One thing that is known certainly reinforces this theory. The formation of diamonds requires enormous pressures and temperatures, and these conditions can only be fulfilled in nature deep in the earth.

The diamond-mining operations as they are carried out in South Africa have changed. In the early days, the broken pieces of the rocky blue ground were spread out for a period of one or two years, when exposure to weather and frequent rolling and turning broke down the substance. Today, the blue ground is no longer left to the influence of the weather. Instead, the rock is passed through heavy rollers provided with special springs in order to avoid breaking any large diamonds. The crushed rocks are then passed to large washing pans so that all mud and lighter materials can be washed away.

Formerly the diamonds had to be picked out by hand from the concentrates. Then, one day, an employee of a large mining company made a remarkable discovery. He found that of all the constituents of the blue ground, the diamond alone adheres to grease more readily than to water.

25. Laying fuses before blasting diamond-bearing blue ground at the Premier Mine

26. African mine workers loading blue ground containing diamonds into trucks underground in a diamond mine in Kimberley

Now, therefore, the crushed-rock mixture is washed over a series of galvanized-iron trays that are covered with a thick coating of grease. The trays are constantly agitated, and the diamonds adhere to the grease while all other materials are washed away with the waters. At frequent intervals, the grease tables are scraped and the diamonds removed. Certain other gem stones may also adhere to the grease, but these can afterward be separated from the diamonds easily by hand.

Diamond crystals are usually quite small and rarely weigh more than

⅕ gram, or one *carat* (28.35 grams, or 141.75 carats, is equal to one ounce avoirdupois). Larger stones may be of great value, but much will depend upon their color and freedom from flaws. With the exception of the rare and unusual colors, such as pink and blue, the colorless stones and those with a faint blue tinge are the most sought after. Unfortunately, most diamonds have a yellow or brownish tinge that reduces their value considerably in the eyes of the jeweler. Faulty stones and those that are badly discolored are used as bort in industry where their extreme hardness allows them to perform many useful functions.

Many famous diamonds have been found throughout the ages, but the

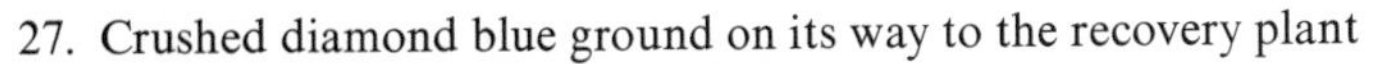

27. Crushed diamond blue ground on its way to the recovery plant

28. Removing diamonds from a grease table

largest and most famous of all is the Cullinan gem, which was discovered in a mine near Pretoria in the Transvaal in 1905. It weighed 3,106 carats, or slightly over 1⅓ pounds. The mine superintendent who found this colossal stone embedded in the rock of the mine face thought at first it was a chunk of glass. He could not believe that so huge a diamond could exist. It was sold to the Transvaal government for £150,000 and later was presented as a gift to Edward VII (1841–1910) who entrusted it to an Amsterdam firm for cutting. They cleaved and cut the perfectly clear and colorless stone into 9 large and 96 small brilliants. The largest of them,

Cullinan I, a drop-shaped stone weighing 530 carats, is the biggest cut diamond in the world. Known as the Star of Africa, it forms part of the British crown jewels and reposes in the Tower of London in the head of the sovereign's scepter. Cullinan II, the second largest of these diamonds, is set in the Imperial State Crown. It is a square-shaped brilliant and weighs 317 carats. Two other large stones, weighing 94 and 63 carats, respectively, and known as Cullinan III and IV, were set in the late Queen Mary's crown for her coronation in 1911. The remaining 5 of the large stones range in weight from 18 carats to 4 carats.

Among other famous diamonds, the Koh-i-Noor deserves special men-

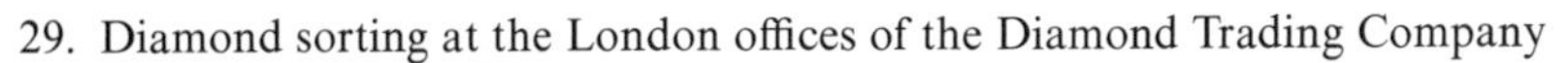
29. Diamond sorting at the London offices of the Diamond Trading Company

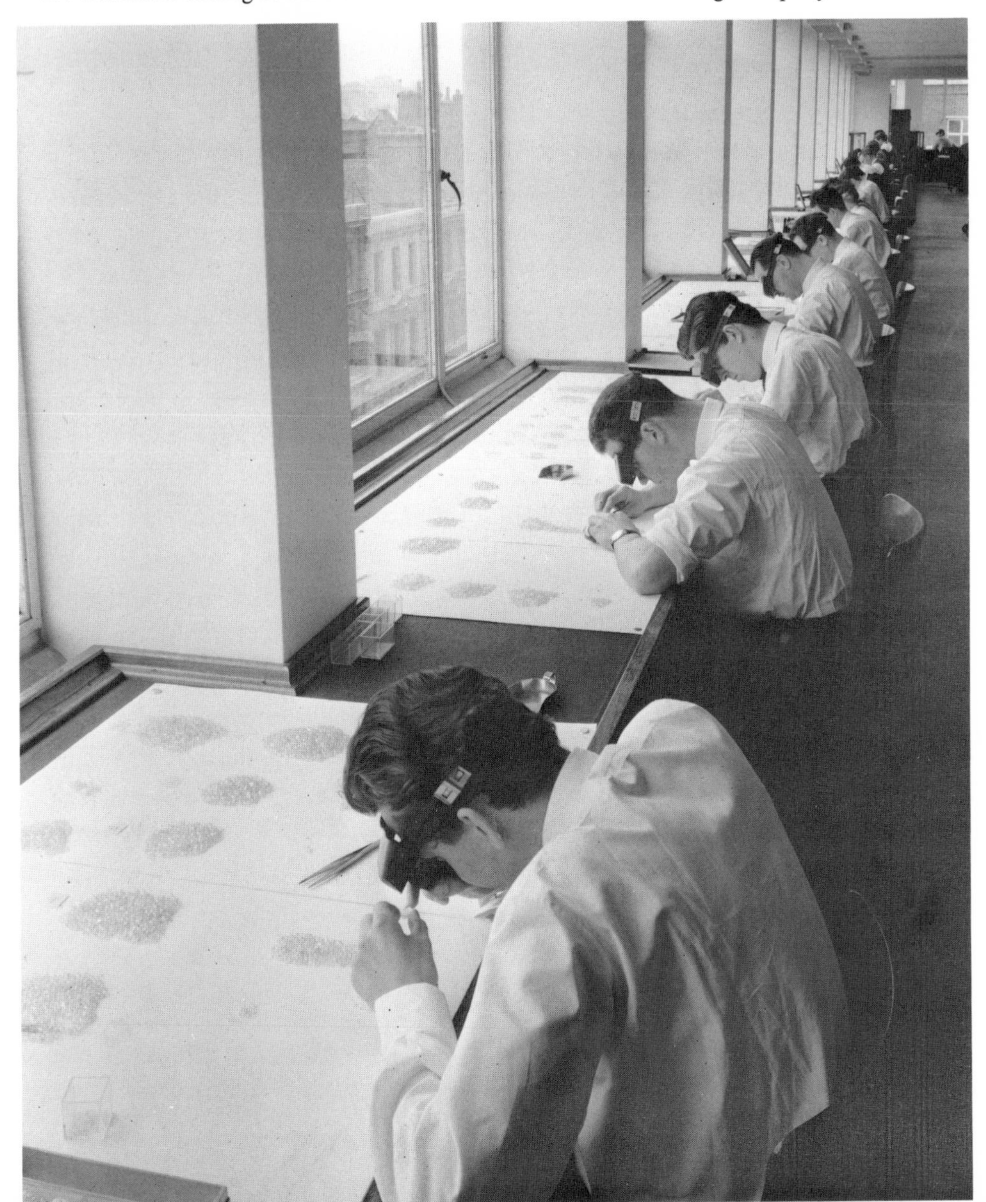

30. The Cullinan diamond: the world's largest diamond as it appeared in the rough, and four of the nine principal stones cut from it

tion. It originated in India and, unlike the Cullinan gem, can claim a long and turbulent history. This famous stone first appeared on the scene early in the fourteenth century, but, according to legend, it may have been known some hundreds of years before that. Historians tell us that the Koh-i-Noor weighed some 800 carats when found in the Golconda mines in southern India. It remained the property of a line of Indian princes until early in the sixteenth century when the Moguls conquered India. Then, the stone fell into the hands of the Mogul emperor and remained in Delhi, where it is said to have adorned the great peacock throne. Later, in 1739, when the Persian conqueror Nadir Shah invaded Delhi, the capture of the diamond was one of his prime objectives. When he had achieved this, he took it back with him to Persia, where it remained until his assassination.

The succeeding years brought a number of wars and revolutions, but the stone was always treasured by the ruling princes until, eventually, it found its way to Lahore, the capital of the Punjab. After the end of the second Sikh war in 1849, the East India Company acquired the diamond. A year later, it was presented to Queen Victoria, who allowed it to be shown at the Great Exhibition in London in 1851.

Because of its lack of sparkle, the stone was recut into an improved shape. This action has since been much criticized, for the process reduced the weight of the stone from 191 carats to 109 carats. Although somewhat improved, it still lacked the fire of a correctly proportioned brilliant-cut diamond. It was set in a brooch for Queen Victoria, and, after her death, adorned the crown of Queen Alexandra. Today, it is set in the centerpiece of the queen-consort's crown.

Another stone worthy of mention is the blue Hope diamond, weighing 44½ carats. This magnificently colored stone is said to originate from a much larger one, the "Tavernier Blue," which used to belong to the imperial French collection. It was stolen in 1790 but reappeared mysteriously on the London diamond market some 40 years later as a smaller stone.

31. The Cullinan diamond after the cleaving process

There seems little doubt that the Hope diamond was a part of the Tavernier Blue that had been stolen, for its color was identical, and large blue diamonds are extremely rare. It was purchased for the sum of £18,000 by the British banker, H. T. Hope, who eventually sold it to the Sultan of Turkey for £80,000. Later it returned to the United States and became the property of the well-known diamond merchant, Harry Winston, who presented it to the Smithsonian Institution in 1958. Today, its value is estimated at some £300,000 ($900,000).

Another notable diamond is the Great Mogul. An Indian stone weighing nearly 800 carats, it was first seen in 1665. The diamond is believed to have been among the booty seized by Nadir Shah when he overran Delhi in 1739. Later, it disappeared completely from the scene, and some authorities believe that another stone, the Orloff diamond, is the Great Mogul. The Orloff weighs almost 200 carats and is a diamond of first-class quality, with the faint bluish tint so highly prized among gem diamonds. It now forms part of the national state jewels of Russia.

Finally, a word about a pink diamond discovered by J. T. Williamson in Tanganyika (now Tanzania) in 1940. Pink diamonds are very rare, and this rose-colored jewel, weighing 54 carats in its uncut state, is one of the largest pink diamonds so far discovered. It was cut into a 23-carat brilliant that adorns the center of an alpine-rose brooch belonging to Elizabeth II.

As has been mentioned, because of its extreme hardness the diamond has a great importance in modern industry. Industrial diamonds do not have the glamorous history of the gem diamonds, but they have made a significant contribution to science and technology. Not only does their hardness make them admirably suited to cut metals of various kinds, but they also form one of the most important factors in precision engineering today.

32. The Hope diamond

Bloodstone	Moss Agate	Onyx
Sapphire crystal		Blue Topaz crystal
Ruby crystal	Black Opal	Red Spinel crystal
		Chrysoprase
Emerald crystal in matrix	Cornelian	Parti-colored Tourmaline crystal

33. The Koh-i-Noor diamond

There are two main qualities of industrial stones, each being marketed for specific industrial purposes. Better quality industrial diamonds are used largely in lathe tools as drilling material and for a great number of high-precision industrial instruments. The lower quality industrial stones, bort, are crushed and graded into so-called mesh sizes to be employed in grinding-wheel stones, cutting saws, and boring tools.

Springing from the great variety of uses for diamond mesh is a recently developed process for smoothing concrete airport runways for high-speed jet aircraft. Crushed bort is also used to grind, polish, and bevel glass, as well as for the polishing of ceramics, plastics, stone, asbestos, cement, and other nonmetallic minerals and materials. Fine diamond powder, a by-product of the crushed bort, is extensively used in all types of lapidary and polishing operations. Large quantities are employed in the watch industry for the boring and shaping of synthetic rubies and sapphires. The mining industry uses diamond drill crowns to drill for oil and many other minerals and for long-hole drilling during shaft sinking and other mining operations.

The demand for the diamond in industry is a comparatively recent development, which received a strong stimulus during the last war when precision instruments of all kinds were urgently needed. To date, the United States is the largest consumer of industrial diamonds, taking about 60 per cent of the total world output. Other large consumers are Great Britain and the other European nations, but an increased demand is developing generally throughout the world.

Because diamonds have, for hundreds of years, been highly prized as gems, it has been the ambition of chemists to produce this magnificent gem artificially. Yet, although the diamond consists of only the element carbon,

34. The sovereign's scepter showing the Cullinan I

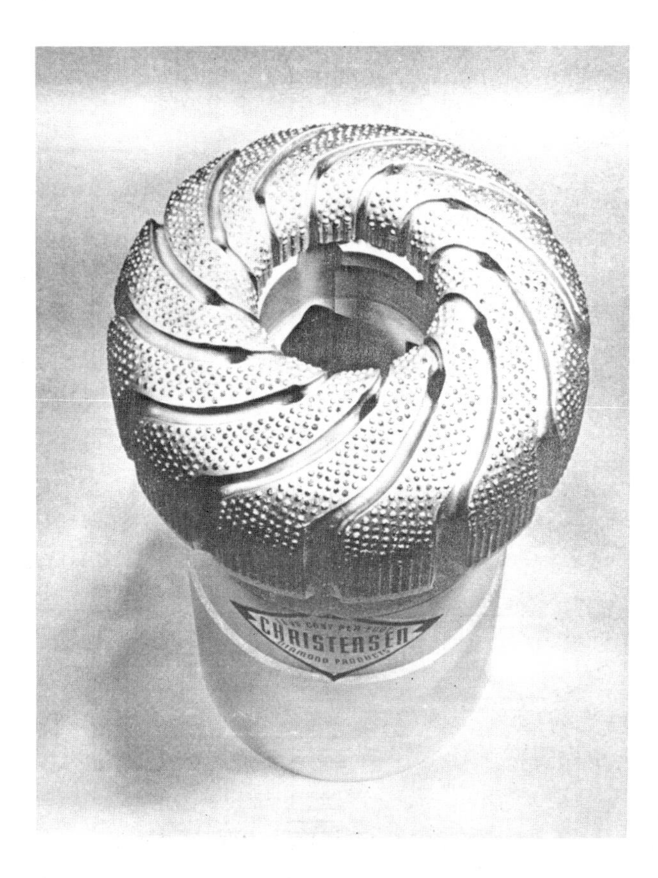

35. A core drill crown set with about 2,500 diamonds

this has proved to be an extremely difficult task, and it was not until 1955 that General Electric and, more recently, De Beers Mining Corporation of South Africa succeeded in producing diamonds on a commercial scale. The commercially produced stones in no way resemble the gems worn as jewelry. Most of them are quite tiny and measure less than 1/250 inch. But even such tiny diamonds are of great value to industry.

The question of why diamonds are so difficult to produce artificially becomes less puzzling if one remembers how tightly the atoms are packed together in the diamond crystal. In graphite and other forms of carbon, this is not the case, and one of the problems that faces the scientists is how to press the carbon atoms sufficiently tightly together so that they will adhere permanently.

In nature, this process goes on deep in the earth, where enormous temperatures and pressures are developed. It was not until scientists were able to devise pressure chambers that could withstand pressures of similar magnitude at very high temperatures that the first successes in synthetic-diamond production were achieved. Figure 36 shows a 1,000-ton diamond-making press in the General Electric research laboratory that can develop pressures greater than 1,500,000 pounds per square inch at temperatures in excess of 2,700° centigrade.

With the rapid advance of science and technology, the day may not be too distant when it will be possible to produce even large jewel diamonds synthetically, but it is unlikely that scientists will not be able to tell the difference between the natural and synthetic.

36. Diamond-making press at the General Electric Research Laboratory

IV

OTHER IMPORTANT GEM STONES

Rubies and Sapphires

The ruby and sapphire share with the diamond, the emerald, and the pearl the position of the most precious jewels in the world. However, the arbitrary distinction between precious and semiprecious stones should be approached with caution since the desirability of any particular gem will depend largely on the prevailing fashions. What may be precious and much sought after in one period of history may have to give way to some rival at a later date. The leading position of these five gems has so far remained unassailed, and, while there may be times when one of them becomes more fashionable than the others, their beauty and rarity have assured them a permanent place among the first five.

Chemically, rubies and sapphires are composed of the simple compound, aluminum oxide, known as *corundum,* which has the formula Al_2O_3. Corundum occurs in nature in a startling variety of colors, and both rubies and sapphires are chemically the same substance; their names merely indicate their different colors.

On the hardness scale, corundum immediately follows diamond, and is thus the second hardest mineral in the world. In its natural form, corundum is found in well-shaped crystals that belong to the *trigonal crystal system.*

Broadly speaking, gem corundum can be divided into two groups: (1) all material that is truly red in color and that is called rubies, and (2) all the many other shades known as sapphires.

Pure corundum is rarely found in nature in a clear form. Moreover, because of its lack of color and sparkle, pure corundum is rarely cut as a gem, and most so-called white sapphires used in cheap jewelry are of synthetic origin. Yet, if small traces of a chemical substance known as chromic oxide, Cr_2O_3, intrude into the crystal structure of the hitherto colorless corundum, it turns red and is transformed into a ruby. Its beauty, however, does not depend on the red color alone, but involves one more of the mysteries of light, known as *fluorescence.* This phenomenon can be illustrated by shining a beam of blue light on a ruby in an otherwise darkened room and then viewing it through a red filter. Normally, if one looks through a red filter at an object illuminated only with blue light, practically nothing will be visible because the red filter will have absorbed all the blue light rays and none of them will be able to reach the eyes. But the ruby is an exception, and it suddenly glows in the dark like a piece of red-hot coal. The explanation is that the ruby has the ability to absorb the shorter blue and violet wave lengths of light and re-emit them as red light of a longer wave length. The fine fluorescent glow can also be stimulated by the ultraviolet rays present in sunlight, which incidentally are the same rays that can cause sunburn.

The ruby is not the only gem stone that has these fluorescent qualities. Many others of quite different composition show a similar phenomenon, but it must be remembered that fluorescence is not an essential property of any of the gems, and it may vary considerably from stone to stone. Many diamonds, for instance, display a sky-blue fluorescence when subjected to ultraviolet radiation, and this may vary from faint to brilliant. These gems are, in fact, so inconsistent in their response that it has been suggested this strange property might be used as a means of identifying pieces of diamond jewelry by photographing them under ultraviolet rays—a kind of fingerprinting process.

The best color in ruby is a deep, rich red, and the finest stones originate in Burma. They are found in crystalline limestone deposits that have been broken down by the influence of weather into a brownish clay from which the ruby crystals are mined. There are other sources—notably Ceylon—where rubies are found in what are called *gem gravels.* These consist of a multitude of different rock materials that have been collected over a period of thousands of years by rivers and mountain streams and are washed into the valleys to be deposited in layers and terraces. Ceylon gem gravels are particularly rich in gem minerals and form one of the richest sources in the world.

37. Simple sifting methods for gem gravels in Ceylon

Picking gem stones from tons of gravel may seem rather a tedious job, yet it is by far the most productive method, and a little consideration will show why. Mining direct from rocks entails the cumbersome operation of crushing the stones and concentrating them artificially before they will yield up their gems—rather like diamond mining from dry diggings. In the case of gem gravels, however, this breaking-up process has already been done by rain, wind, and frost. Further, some of the lighter rock materials will have been washed away by the action of rivers and streams, leaving the heavier materials to sink to the bottom. Since many gem materials fall into the heavier category, these gravels will contain a high proportion of a variety of gem stones.

As with the ruby, the color of sapphires is due to small quantities of chemical impurities. These may take the form of titanium oxide and a trace of iron oxide. Few people realize that sapphires can have many different hues and the general belief that sapphires can only be blue is quite incorrect. There are green, yellow, purple, and pink stones, with many intermediate shades. All of them owe their hues to small quantities of chemical impurities that were present in the aluminum oxide when it formed into crystals many millions of years ago. But, as with most other gem stones, the crucial factor that ultimately determines their value is not their chemical composition—important as this is when identifying them—but their appearance. The most valuable sapphires are those of a fine blue color, and the best of them are found in Thailand. In Burma, they are found in association with ruby, and some of them can be of fine quality, while others may be so deeply colored that they appear almost black. Other localities where sapphires are found include India, Australia, the United States, and Ceylon. Ceylon gem gravels are particularly rich in sapphires, and many of the green, yellow, and fancy-colored stones come from there.

There is yet one more gem variety about which so far nothing has been said. This variety is known as the *star stones,* which description reveals much of their peculiar properties. If a piece of star corundum is correctly cut and polished, with a rounded dome-shaped cabochon top, it will reveal a clearly marked six-rayed star on its curved surface. Usually, the color of these star rubies and sapphires is not as attractive as that of the more common stones, and they are not transparent, but this is compensated for by the attractive star that sparkles on their surfaces.

The secret of this play of light lies within the rough corundum crystals. Try to imagine that such crystals contain three sets of parallel, silklike

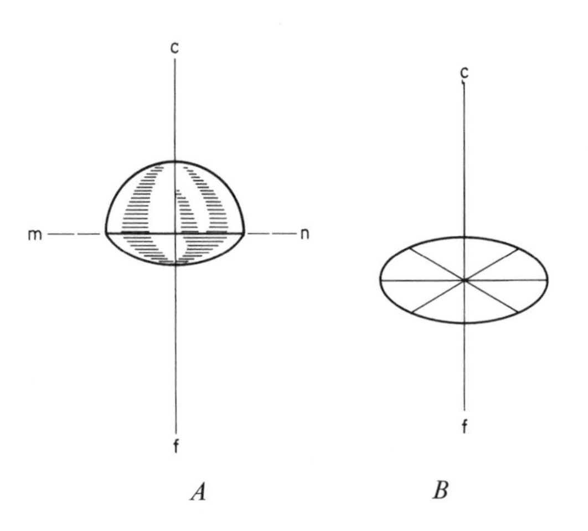

38. The star stones. In *A*, the stone is cut cabochon so that the vertical crystal axis, *cf*, passes through the top of the dome. The three sets of silk inclusions lie at right angles to the vertical axis, and intersect at angles of 60°; *B* shows the directions of the silk inclusions, or cavities

bundles of fine fibers that extend throughout the stone and intersect one another at angles of 60°. They may consist of fine needles of another mineral known as *rutile,* or they may be formed from ultrafine hollow tubes, or even from tiny particles which could not be seen under the microscope. These bundles of fibers are arranged in such a manner that they lie parallel to the lateral axes of the stone and at right angles to the vertical axis (see Fig. 38). The stone must be cut in such a manner that its long verical axis passes through the center of the dome-shaped top, thus making the silk fibers lie parallel to the flat girdle plane of the stone.

The first successful attempt to produce rubies and sapphires synthetically was made in the early part of this century by a Frenchman whose name was Auguste Verneuil (1856–1913). He invented a special apparatus generally known today as the *Verneuil Chalumeau* (see Fig. 39). He used as his raw material pure alumina powder (aluminum oxide) to which was added 2½ per cent chromic oxide to produce the red color of the ruby. The mixture was placed into the apparatus, consisting essentially of two tubes. The upper tube, *X*, is wider above and constricted below and passes down the center of the lower tube, *Y*. It terminates just above the opening of *Y* in a fine nozzle. Oxygen is admitted through tube *A*. Vessel *C* carries the alumina powder and has at its base a cylindrical sieve of fine mesh. *B* is a small hammer that is operated at regular intervals, and a succession of rapid taps causes the alumina powder to fall down the tube. The amount is regulated by the varying height from which the hammer falls. Hydrogen is admitted through tube *D* into outer tube *Y*. The oxygen and hydrogen gases mix and are ignited at the outlet of tube *X*. As the powder reaches the outlet of tube *X*, it is melted by the intensely hot flame and falls upon the pedestal *F*, where the *boule* begins to grow. When the rounded crystal column, the boule (see Fig. 40) has reached the required size, the gases are cut off. *E* is a fire-clay screen surrounding the flame, with an opening in the front for viewing the boule during growth. As the boule grows, it can be lowered slowly by a screw arrangement at *G*.

While Verneuil was operating the device, a peculiar thing happened. As the molten mass began to cool on the fire-clay pedestal it did not return to its original powder form, but began to grow as a crystal, each cooling drop crystallizing in the proper alignment as it solidified. In outward appearance it bore little resemblance to a crystal because it was shaped like a rounded column with a narrow base, but, apart from its shape, it possessed all the properties of a natural ruby.

Verneuil's production methods have hardly been changed to the present day. Synthetic sapphires are manufactured by a similar process, and, by adding different chemical compounds to the alumina powder, a large variety of colors can be produced.

Fortunately, it is possible to distinguish natural rubies and sapphires from their synthetic cousins; the methods used are discussed in Chapter VII. Most of the commercial production of synthetic corundum is directed toward industry where its great hardness serves many uses. The bearings of better quality watches and those of many precision instruments are made from synthetic corundum. When reference is made to a 13-jewel watch, this actually means that the device contains 13 bearings made from synthetic corundum. Pick-up heads of modern phonographs are frequently fitted either with diamond or synthetic-corundum needles because of their extreme hardness and durability. When found in its impure form, naturally mixed with magnetite, corundum is known as emery and serves as an important polishing agent for all types of metal and stone work.

A more recent and exciting scientific and industrial use for synthetic

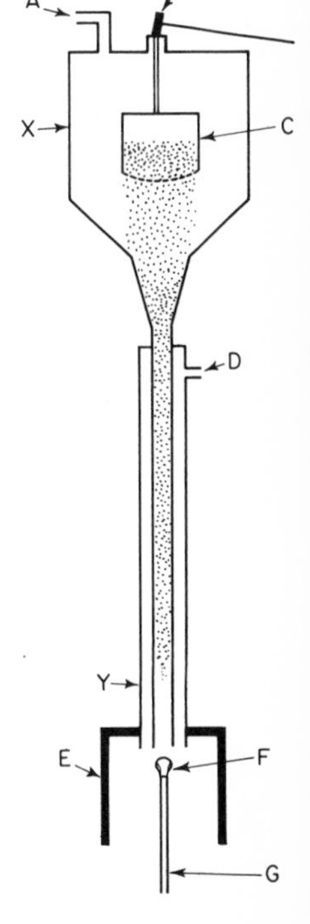

39. The Verneuil Chalumeau

corundum is in connection with the production of *laser* beams. In 1960, a group of scientists working for the Hughes Aircraft Corporation in California discovered that an input of light energy into a synthetic ruby rod energized the chromium atoms that give the ruby its characteristic red color, causing them to emit pure red light of a fixed wave length, which emerges in the form of a nearly parallel beam from the end of the rod. It was pointed out earlier that natural or synthetic rubies will emit red light if suitably stimulated, but what makes the laser beam so special is that the chromium atoms inside the ruby rod emit red light in unison instead of at random. The name "laser" is an acronym of the somewhat cumbersome phrase *l*ight *a*mplification by *s*timulated *e*mission of *r*adiation. This gives a clue to the origin of the powerful laser beam.

The technical principle is relatively simple. Mirrors are placed at either end of the ruby rod, and, as soon as the flash from a discharge lamp energizes some of the chromium atoms within the rod, the light they emit is reflected backward and forward by the mirrors, building up in intensity as it stimulates other chromium atoms to emit in step; that is, the atoms emit light so that the peaks of the wave length come at the same instant. The result is a tremendous, but very short, burst of energy lasting only a fraction of a second. If suitably focused with an ordinary lens, a laser pulse can blast a hole through a ⅛-inch-thick sheet of steel. The heat created is

40. Synthetic boules

tremendous, and the temperature in the minute area where the laser beam is focused rises almost instantaneously to many thousands of degrees centigrade. This concentrated source of energy has been applied successfully to a variety of scientific and industrial processes, ranging from surgery to communications. In the latter field, a laser beam replacing conventional cables can carry thousands of telephone conversations inside a pipe line, and, in this connection, experiments are currently being conducted by the Bell Telephone Company. Machines have also been devised to allow lasers to be used during delicate operations of the eye, and eye surgeons have successfully welded detached retinas back into place by means of a laser beam.

Promising experiments are also being conducted to apply the power of the laser to drill hard substances. Holes can be punched into diamonds, and the beam can be used to drill synthetic corundum used in bearings.

Most of the technological and medical applications of the laser beam are as yet in an experimental stage, but there is little doubt that in time this remarkable source of energy will play an increasingly important part in future industrial and scientific development.

Emeralds and Aquamarines

Emeralds and aquamarines originate from the same mineral. Chemically, they consist of four elements, beryllium, aluminum, silicon, and oxygen, which have entered into a complex combination to form the mineral beryl. Whether the resultant stones are emerald green, aquamarine blue, or even pink or yellow once again depends upon the extent of the chemical impurities present in the crystals.

The value of the emerald does, of course, depend largely upon its color. Indeed, unless it is a vivid green it cannot be classed as an emerald at all. If the mineral is pale green and the crystal clear, it is not an emerald but simply green beryl. Once, a beryl crystal was found in Norway that measured more than 5 feet in length and weighed over 2 tons, but unfortunately it was not an emerald nor was it even transparent. It was simply the mineral beryl, in its commonest form (see Fig. 41). Huge opaque crystals of beryl have been found in various parts of the world.

Emeralds and aquamarines occur in nature as beautifully formed hexagonal crystals (see Fig. 10). They have a hardness of 7¾, which is only just sufficient to protect them from undue wear and tear when worn as jewelry. This may seem confusing at first, since 7¾ seems quite high up on the hardness scale. There is, however, a mineral known as quartz, which possesses a hardness of 7. In its commonest form it is found almost everywhere. Much of the sand on the beaches, as well as the materials used for making roads, contains it, while fine particles of it float all around us in the air as part of ordinary dust. As such, it comes into contact with everything, including jewelry, and in the course of time it will scratch and wear away those materials that are softer than itself. It is wise, therefore, when purchasing jewelry, to know the hardness of the gems it may contain. Disappointment will be great if you buy a ring containing a beautiful gem stone that, after a short period of wear, loses its polish and shows signs of scratching.

A good example of this is the stone known as strontium titanate, $SrTiO_3$. This is a man-made gem synthesized in the laboratory, and it resembles the diamond in almost every detail. It sparkles even more beautifully than the diamond, but its hardness is only 6, and it is therefore liable to lose its polish quickly if frequently worn, especially in rings where the stone comes into contact with many objects during wear.

Unlike other gem stones, emeralds are not generally found in sands and gravels but are mined almost always from the parent rock. The reasons for this are that emerald is a relatively light stone and therefore more likely to be washed away by rivers and streams. The crystals are often fractured owing to geological upheavals that the parent rock has undergone.

Today, the most important source of emeralds is at Muzo in the Republic of Colombia in South America. It is here that the largest and most beautiful stones are found. The mines are exceedingly old and were known to the ancient civilization of the Incas. The Spanish conquerors seem to have been

41. Hexagonal crystal of the mineral beryl in its commonest form

42. Natural emeralds from the Muzo Mine in Colombia, the source of the world's finest emeralds

the first Europeans to learn about the Colombian emerald treasures. After having plundered many magnificent stones possessed by the native population, they set about searching for their source and eventually, in 1558, discovered some of the mines.

Emeralds are also found in the Ural Mountains of Russia, in Egypt, and in India, and recently, some very fine stones have been mined in Southern Rhodesia. Even in Europe, where few gem stones originate, there is an area in the Austrian Alps, known as Habachtal, where emeralds occur. Unfortunately, it is not very productive and is rarely worked.

Very few emeralds are completely clear and transparent, but such stones are immensely valuable. The gems usually contain certain irregularities known scientifically as *inclusions.* These inclusions may consist of cavities of tiny bubbles of gas, or they may be tiny foreign mineral crystals that were trapped in the crystal when it was originally formed. Inclusions are of great interest to the gemmologist, for in some cases they form a guide as to the origin of the stones. For example, if a certain stone when examined under the microscope revealed toothed cavities, as shown in Fig. 43, it could be deduced immediately that it came from emerald mines in Colombia, where stones with these inclusions are found.

Aquamarine, unlike the emerald, is normally found in clear, transparent crystals. Indeed, the value of these stones is much reduced if they contain irregularities. Principal sources are an area known as Minas Gerais in Brazil, Madagascar, and Ceylon. Color varies from pale blue to greenish blue, and the value of aquamarines as gems will largely depend on their transparency, color, and size. Blue-green stones can be changed to blue, the ideal color, if carefully heated; but this operation must be left to the skilled technician, otherwise the stone may be spoiled. Similar color changes in a number of minerals can be induced by careful heating.

Other kinds of beryl used in jewelry are its pink form, known as morganite, and its yellow-green form, known as heliodor. The former is found in California and Madagascar, and the latter in the United States, West Africa, and Ceylon.

Like diamonds and rubies, emeralds, too, enjoy great popularity as gem stones, and, for many years, more or less successful attempts have been made to synthesize them in the laboratory. Today, they are mostly produced in San Francisco by the chemist Carroll S. Chatham. The exact process employed by him is still shrouded in secrecy, but the principle employed is believed to be an improvement of the flux-melt method in which the components are dissolved in a crucible, and, when the tempera-

43. Three-phase inclusions in a Colombian emerald, as seen under the microscope. Note the liquid-filled, spikey-edged cavities containing cubic mineral crystals and gas bubbles

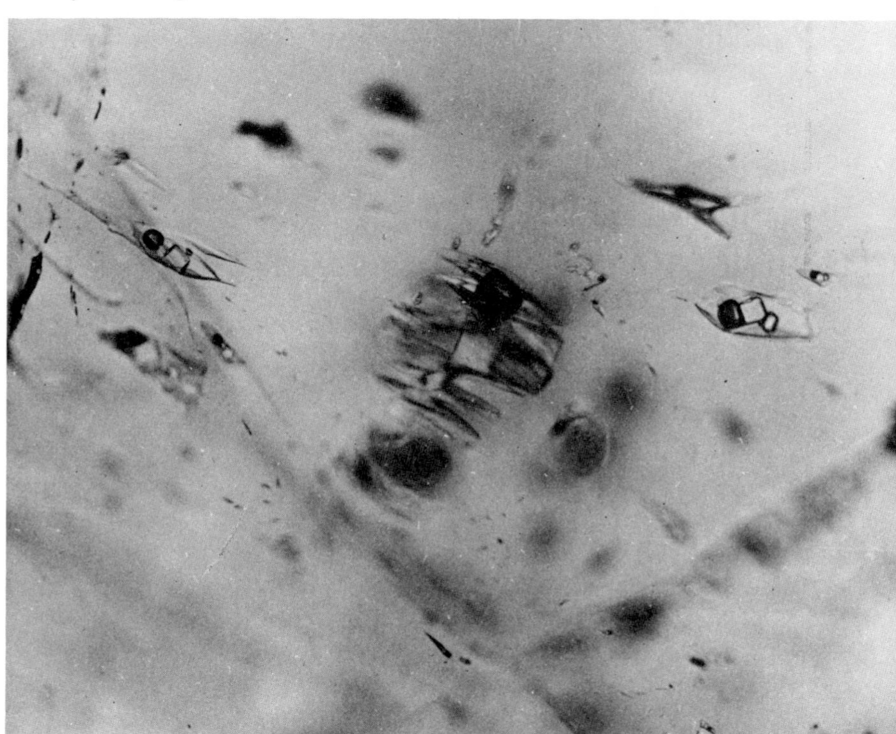

44. Carroll S. Chatham preparing a chemical nutrient solution for the "growth" of his synthetic emeralds

ture is carefully reduced, a crystal forms, sinks to the bottom of the crucible and continues to grow there.

Another method of making emeralds is similar in many ways to the production of synthetic quartz crystals. The principal apparatus employed consists of a chamber known as an *autoclave,* or *bomb,* capable of withstanding enormous pressures. This chamber is filled with water and some fragments of quartz crystals. It is then tightly shut and the bottom portion is heated by means of an electric current to a temperature of 365° centigrade. This is more than three times the temperature at which water boils, but the nature of quartz is such that it requires this high temperature before it will dissolve freely in water.

In order to grow the quartz crystals, the top of the vessel is kept at a lower temperature than the bottom, and, as the solution is circulated from the bottom to the top, the water at the top of the autoclave can no longer hold the quartz in solution, and it is deposited in the form of crystals. These crystals grow very slowly, and the process takes a number of weeks to complete.

Synthetic emerald crystals fortunately can be distinguished from the natural stones by careful examination and testing, but the outward appearance of the synthetic stones can be most attractive and is in most ways similar to the natural stones.

45. Synthetic Chatham emerald crystals and cut stones

The metal beryllium has great industrial importance. A white metal that does not occur in nature in a pure state, it is obtained by the electrolysis of its fused compounds. Lighter than aluminum, it is used in the production of special alloys together with copper, iron, and nickel. The ore from which beryllium derives is beryl in its impure form.

Topaz

Topaz has always been a well-known and popular gem stone, and it is associated with a fine yellow, or sherry, color. It is frequently worn in rings, brooches, and pendants, and in antique jewelry large, transparent, flawless stones are especially common. The name topaz has caused a good deal of confusion in the past, since not so long ago it used to be common practice to apply it to almost all yellow gems irrespective of their true identity. Thus, the beautiful yellow form of corundum that should properly be called a yellow sapphire is on occasion misleadingly called topaz. Quartz, too, can be found in a clear yellow form, known as citrine, and this is frequently called topaz and sold as such. In this instance the unsuspecting purchaser will make a bad bargain, since citrine is a much inferior, and far less valuable, stone than the true topaz. It is quite wrong to give the name topaz to any other gem stone but the true one, and, fortunately, this conception is beginning to gain general acceptance among jewelers all over the world.

Topaz occurs in nature in the form of well-shaped crystals belonging to the orthorhombic crystal system (see Fig. 12). It is a complicated fluosilicate of aluminum, and its chemical formula is written as $Al_2(FOH)_2SiO_4$. It is one of the few gem minerals that contain the element fluorine (F).

Topaz has a hardness index of 8 and is therefore harder than the mineral quartz. It is admirably suited as a gem stone that will stand up to wear over long periods of time. The state of Minas Gerais in Brazil produces the finest of the yellow- and sherry-colored stones, but fine blue and white topazes are also found in the gem gravels of Ceylon. Other sources are the Ural Mountains in Russia, where fine blue stones are found, and the United States, where occasional finds have been made, notably in the state of Colorado. Topaz is also one of the few gems that have, on occasion, been found in the form of pale blue water-worn crystals in the Cairngorm district of Scotland.

Like the emerald, ruby, and sapphire, topaz displays its beauty by virtue of its attractive color and not by its fire, as the diamond does. Its dispersion is small, and it is unable to split white light into the spectrum colors to any appreciable extent.

On occasion, pink topaz is displayed in jewelry, but such stones most likely had their color artifically induced by the careful heating of yellow- or sherry-colored stones under controlled conditions, for pink topaz rarely occurs in nature. This color change can be traced to a rearrangement of the atoms within the crystal. It is interesting to note that not every yellow topaz will change to pink on heating, but only sherry-hued stones of Brazilian origin.

Spinel

As a gem, spinel can be regarded as a sort of poor relation of the ruby. At its best, it occurs as a perfectly transparent red stone closely resembling the ruby, and, for this reason, red spinels are sometimes wrongly referred to as spinel rubies or balas rubies. This name, however, should not be used, for, apart from its color, spinel has little in common with the ruby and is in fact a different mineral.

Blue spinel is not uncommon in nature, but its color is a not-too-attractive ink shade, and it is rarely used in jewelry.

Like the diamond, spinel belongs to the cubic crystal system and occurs in nature in beautiful octahedral crystals (see Color Plate II). Sometimes, these are so perfectly shaped and possess such lustrous faces that the uninitiated might well think they had been skillfully polished by a craftsman. For this reason, they are sometimes worn as natural crystals in native jewelry.

Chemically, spinel is an oxide of magnesium and aluminum, and its formula is $MgAl_2O_4$. Like ruby, it owes its red color to small traces of chromium. The blue shade is said to be due to traces of iron. With a hardness of 8, spinel ranks among the hardest minerals and, although it is admirably suitable as a ring stone, it is seldom found in sufficiently large sizes for that purpose.

It occurs largely in association with ruby and is found in the ruby-bearing limestones of Burma and Thailand. Attractive violet and blue stones have been discovered in the Ceylon gem gravels, also a black form of spinel called ceylonite. Colorless spinel is rarely found in nature, most of these being produced synthetically as well as in many attractive shades. The process employed is almost identical with that used for synthetic rubies and sapphires, but the raw material in this case consists of a mixture of aluminum and magnesium oxides to which are added the appropriate chemicals to produce the required shades.

In the centerpiece of the British Imperial State Crown is set a marvelous red stone known as the Black Prince's ruby, which is said to date back to the fourteenth century. Many exciting tales have been told about its history. The stone is irregular in shape and measures nearly 2 inches in length. In early times, when all red gems were believed to be rubies, this magnificent stone was so called. Today, however, it is known to be only a red spinel and of inferior value. Yet, in this instance, the true value does not lie with the mineral species to which it belongs, but in its long and ancient history.

46. The Imperial State Crown with Cullinan II and the Black Prince's ruby as centerpiece

Quartz

Quartz is the commonest mineral found on earth. It occurs in an amazing variety of forms. In the world of gem stones, quartz also supplies more different varieties than any other mineral. Chemically, it is simply the oxide of the element silicon, and its chemical formula is SiO_2. Gem quartzes can roughly be divided into three main groups: (1) crystallized quartz, (2) compact quartz, and (3) cryptocrystalline quartz.

The first group comprises transparent crystals that show definite crystal forms. Perhaps the best known of these is the clear and transparent rock crystal, which consists of pure crystalline silica. Incidentally, the word "crystal" originates from the Greek word *krystallos,* meaning ice, for the ancient Greeks thought that these transparent rock crystals were in fact frozen water turned into stone. Today, the main sources of rock crystal are Brazil and Madagascar, but there are also many minor sources widely distributed all over the world. Crystals of brownish color known as cairngorm are also found in the Scottish mountains.

Amethyst, another of the crystallized quartzes, ranges from a lilac shade to a dark, rich purple, and, for many centuries, it has been held in high esteem as a gem of considerable beauty. Its name comes from the Greek and means "not drunk," since in ancient times it was thought that amethysts were a preventive against the effects of alcohol. It has been established to many people's satisfaction that the violet color comes from the combination of iron and irradiation. Amethysts are chiefly found in Brazil, Uruguay, Madagascar, and the Ural Mountains, although stones of inferior color are found in many parts of the world. Aggregates of small impure crystals are sometimes used as paper weights.

Citrine, the yellow form of quartz, may range in color from a pale yellow to a brownish red. It is valued as a gem stone, but is often confused with the much more valuable topaz and is even mistakenly called by that name.

Rose quartz, in delicate shades of pink, may also be classed as a crystalline quartz although it rarely occurs in crystal shapes. It is normally found in massive lumps. The material is translucent and will allow light to pass through it, but it is usually not clear enough to be transparent. Rose quartz has become particularly popular as a medium for carved ornaments and can also be most attractive as beads worn as necklaces and other forms of jewelry. It is found in Brazil, Madagascar, and the United States.

One fine form of quartz, known as tiger eye, is much valued as a gem stone. It is particularly attractive as a ring stone of a brown, silky appearance. If cut cabochon, a single bright line of light will appear on its surface. This is caused by straight fibrous inclusions that run through the stone and can be likened to the ruby and sapphire star stones, in which the effect is produced by similar causes.

The second group, compact quartz, does not consist of large, individual crystals. The best-known form, jasper, consists essentially of an aggregate of tiny quartz grains packed together into massive lumps containing as much as 20 per cent of foreign matter in the form of clay and iron oxide. Even in thin sections this form of quartz is opaque, yet it occurs in many attractive shades such as brown, yellow, red, and green. Jasper is found in many parts of the world and is mostly an ornamental stone that, in ancient times, was much used in the art of engraving.

Aventurine is another of the compact quartzes. Usually green in shade, but on occasions brown and yellow, it contains a mass of tiny mica flakes that give the stone a speckled sheen. Richest sources lie in the Ural Mountains and eastern India. This form of quartz is sometimes most effectively imitated by forms of colored glass containing tiny copper flakes.

Finally come the large group of cryptocrystalline quartzes. *Cryptocrystalline* means made up of hidden crystals, and this is indeed what they are. Cryptocrystalline quartzes consist of a mass of tiny quartz crystals that have formed together into large lumps and show no external crystal form, yet each of the component crystals that makes up the mass is a genuine crystal. These quartzes have been grouped under the general title of chalcedony. The most valuable of the group is one called chrysoprase. It has an apple-green color due to the presence of the metal nickel. Chrysoprase free from faults is rare and highly valued. Like most cryptocrystalline quartzes, it has always been much used for ornamental carved objects and also is an attractive stone for jewelry. Other varieties of chalcedony are: green spotted with red, called bloodstone; orange-red translucent, called carnelian; and deep brown translucent, known as sard.

Among the best-known forms of cryptocrystalline quartzes are the agates. Technically, they are really the same as chalcedony, already referred to, but formed in a special way that makes them attractive. They consist of chalcedony arranged in curved or circular bands. These are made up of various colors of different degrees of transparency. In ancient lava rocks, where the chalcedony was deposited, they were formed in almond-shaped holes. Sometimes, these cavities are not completely filled, and may be lined on the inside with some purple amethyst crystals.

Agates are mostly used for ornamental objects such as ash trays or umbrella handles, and much of this material now is artificially colored with some special dyes. The center of the agate-cutting industry is in Idar-Oberstein in Germany, but most of the agates used there have to be imported from Brazil since German sources have become exhausted.

There are a number of other banded varieties of quartz, one of them being onyx. Here, the bands run in straight lines and usually there is one layer of white adjacent to one layer of black. Such stones have been much used for cameo brooches, where the stones are so cut that a white picture is carved against a black background. Another form is the so-called sardonyx, where red and white bands alternate.

Finally, there is yet another strange, but exciting, form known as moss agate. It is white or gray in color with internal black or greenish markings resembling strange plants or little trees. An important source for it is India.

The industrial uses of quartz are numerous and important. As material for lenses, quartz can replace glass when superior hardness is called for to resist scratching and undue wear. Quartz is also more transparent to ultraviolet radiation than ordinary glass and can be used in specialized photographic equipment where lenses with such transparency are of importance.

When crystalline quartz is fused in an intensely hot oxyhydrogen flame, silica glass is formed. This differs in its physical properties from the crystalline variety in that it has a lower specific gravity and refractive index, and its hardness is reduced to 5 on Mohs' scale. It is singly refractive and thus unable to split light rays like the crystalline form. Its importance to science and industry lies in the fact that, unlike most other glasses, it can withstand sudden large temperature changes without risk of fracture. This allows it to be used extensively in the construction of crucibles and other laboratory apparatus.

Another important use of crystalline quartz lies in the field of radio broadcasting. It was discovered that physical pressure on a crystal slab induces opposite electrical charges on the opposite faces; the charges are reversed when the crystals are stretched. This phenomenon is known as *piezoelectricity*. Conversely, a thin crystal slab placed into an alternating electric field can be made to oscillate. During the last war these properties were developed extensively for use in radio apparatus to control the frequency of radio circuits. Thin plates are cut from untwinned pure quartz crystals and used as oscillator plates in the radio equipment. Supplies of suitable quartz for this purpose are derived mainly from Brazil, but much of this material is today produced synthetically.

Quartz sand is used extensively as an abrasive on sandpapers, in glass-making, and in scouring powder. It also forms an essential constituent of many materials used in the building industry.

Zircon

The mineral zircon has quite often been used in jewelry to simulate the diamond. However, it is hardly ever found in nature in a colorless state.

Chemically, zircon is the silicate of the element zirconium in company with traces of uranium, and its formula is written as $ZrSiO_4$. Normally, it is found in well-shaped crystals belonging to the tetragonal crystal system (see Fig. 8). These crystals are usually a reddish-brown shade, although sometimes their color is a yellowish-green. The reason for this variation is that zirconium silicate occurs in what is known as the high and low forms. The former constitute the brown variety, while the latter are the green stones.

The explanation of high and low lies in their physical properties. For example, the high form has a greater *specific gravity* than its low relative, which means that if a high and a low stone are of identical size, the high form will weigh more than the low form. High zircons are also strongly double refractive, whereas the low types show far less of this property (see Chapter VII).

What are the reasons why the same mineral can behave so differently? Again, the explanation is within the crystals themselves and the way their atoms are arranged.

It has been mentioned already that zircon contains small traces of the element uranium or thorium—which is associated with radioactivity in one form or another. In the low-type zircons, the orderly arrangement of atoms within the crystal has partially collapsed due to radioactivity. This collapse is brought about by the discharge of *alpha particles* (the nuclei of helium atoms) from the radioactive element, which displace some of the atoms within the zircon crystal. Some low zircons can be restored to the high form by heating them to a high temperature, but exactly why this takes place in some stones and not in others is not known.

Heat has another effect upon the stone. As already indicated, zircons are rarely used in their natural colors in jewelry, most of them being either colorless or a rather beautiful blue color. The desired colors are obtained by a carefully applied heat treatment to which the natural brown stones are subjected and that renders them either colorless or blue. Zircon is essentially an oriental gem stone, and, for years, the Ceylon gem gravels were its only important source. Today, Thailand and Vietnam also produce fine stones. Most of the blue and colorless zircons are heat treated and cut in Bangkok.

Zircon has a hardness of 7½ on the Mohs scale, and, being only slightly harder than quartz, may show wear if worn for long periods as a ring stone. Yet, in an attempt to simulate the diamond, it is often worn as such.

The fire of zircon is inferior to that of a diamond, but, if cut in the same way, it may well fool the unsuspecting into believing that it is the more precious stone. A good magnifying glass, however, will quickly reveal the strong double refraction of zircon—clearly showing two images of the edges between the back facets if the stone is viewed from the front. The diamond, as already pointed out, belongs to the cubic crystal system, the minerals of which show no double refraction. A diamond will show only one image of its back facets when viewed with a lens through the front (see Chapter VII).

Mineral deposits of zircon in Brazil, India, and New South Wales, Australia, have considerable commercial importance as sources of the metal zirconium that, together with its compounds, is becoming increasingly important in industry. The metal is used in alloys and in the purification of steel.

Tourmaline

This romantic-sounding gem stone first appeared on the scene early in the eighteenth century, when merchants from Ceylon brought a parcel of these stones to Europe. Its name is taken from the Sinhalese word *turmali,* meaning "attracter of ashes." If rubbed or heated, tourmaline becomes strongly charged with electricity, and, in this state, will readily attract dust particles. Chemically, it is a highly complex silicate of the elements boron and aluminum with magnesium, iron, and the metals sodium, potassium, and lithium present in varying quantities. Its complex chemical composition can be described by the formula $(Na,Ca)(Li,Mg,Fe,Al)_9B_3Si_6(O,OH)_{31}$.

In its gem varieties, tourmaline produces a galaxy of colors that surpass all other gem minerals in their versatility. Because of this, it has become increasingly popular as a gem stone and, although its hardness is only 7¼, is much worn in rings and brooches. The reason for its great color versatility lies in its varying chemical composition: tourmalines containing iron will usually be black; those containing sodium, potassium, or lithium may be red, green, or colorless. Then again, those containing magnesium will be yellow, brown, or black.

Tourmaline is a common rock-forming mineral and is widely distributed all over the world. Gem-quality stones are found in the Ural Mountains, where magnificent pink, blue, and green crystals have been mined. Other sources are the state of Minas Gerais in Brazil, the islands of Madagascar and Ceylon, and California.

Apart from their rare beauty, tourmaline crystals are often particolored, the two extremities of the slender prismatic crystals exhibiting different hues. Indeed, ring stones where one half of the stone is a soft pink, and the other half the green of the oceans, are sometimes met with. Tourmaline, more than most other doubly refractive gem stones, exhibits a directional property of crystals known as *dichroism,* or the property by which the color of a crystal may vary according to the direction in which it is viewed. This phenomenon is particularly striking in green and brown tourmalines, which in certain directions will prevent all light from penetrating them, but in others will appear transparent and colorful. Tourmaline is therefore yet another gem stone where the knowledge of the lapidarist must be correctly applied so as to obtain the best results when it is cut into a gem.

Opal

The opal is a close relative of quartz. It consists of silica containing a variable percentage of water (8–12 per cent). But, unlike quartz, the silica is noncrystalline, and has solidified into a kind of stone jelly.

Opal counts among the most colorful and effective gem stones. The material itself is almost colorless, and its play of color, which embodies all shades of the spectrum, is caused by the regular arrangement of rows of tiny spheres, which produce this optical effect.

Black opal is particularly valuable. This shows red flashes of light against a dark background. Other forms are white opal, water opal, and fire opal. The fire opal is found in Mexico and looks very different from the other two kinds. Indeed, the layman would hardly recognize it as an opal, since it is clearly transparent and bright orange, with no play of color.

In earlier times, most opals used to come from Hungary, and then, early in this century, the opal fields of Australia were discovered. Today most opals come from that continent. They are found in association with sandstone that has been colored brown by the iron it contains. The opal material (silica) has infiltrated into cracks of the rocks, where it has solidified.

Opal mining is a difficult undertaking, and only a few organized mines exist. Most of the work is done by small groups of prospectors, who look for the precious opals among inhospitable scrub or desert country in Queensland and New South Wales. Since opals are formed within the cracks and cavities of sandstone many a prospector has destroyed a small fortune by striking a boulder a careless blow and thereby shattering what might have been a valuable opal core within the boulder. As with most prospecting of this type, much has to be left to chance. One may strike it rich in a week, or climate and disease may force him to give up altogether without any reward.

Some people consider opal an unlucky gem, and there may be a scientific reason for this belief. Perhaps it lies in the fact that these stones are liable to shatter easily if subjected to sudden shock or even through changes of temperature. Perhaps also, it is because some opals will show their fine fire only after they have been immersed in water. The effect is, however, only temporary and the stone becomes lifeless as the water evaporates.

Opal has a hardness of only 6½ on the Mohs scale, but with reasonable care it should have a long life as a gem stone.

Chrysoberyl

Chrysoberyl is an oxide of the two elements beryllium and aluminum, and its chemical formula is $BeAl_2O_4$. One of the less known and rarer gem stones, it occurs in a variety of yellow to green shades. Its name comes from the Greek word *chrysos,* meaning gold. It is one of the hardest minerals on earth, and its hardness of 8½ on the Mohs scale makes it an ideal gem stone.

More important, however, are its two varieties—chrysoberyl cat's-eye (cymophane) and alexandrite. If cut cabochon, the former shows a bright bluish streak of light running over its surface. This is particularly effective because, unlike quartz cat's-eye, the gems are almost transparent and achieve an ethereal effect. The phenomenon is caused by microscopically small hollow tubes that run parallel through the stone and in most cases are almost impossible to detect. The clearer the streak of light, the more valuable is the stone.

A truly exciting and mysterious gem is the alexandrite, for it appears green by daylight and red in artificial light. These stones owe their color to small quantities of chromic oxide. When light rich in green rays (daylight) falls upon them, they appear green, while artificial light, rich in red rays, makes them appear red. The finest alexandrites are those that are emerald green and ruby red under the correct respective illumination, but such stones are rare and expensive and rank among the finest specimens of gem stones in the world.

The name has its origin in Russia, for, early in the nineteenth century, on the occasion of the coming-of-age ceremony of Tsar Alexander II, such a stone was presented to him as a gift.

The yellow and green chrysoberyl and chrysoberyl cat's-eye are found as pebbles in Brazil and Ceylon. The finest alexandrites occur in the Ural Mountains, often in association with emeralds. Larger alexandrites come from Ceylon, but these stones do not have such an impressive color change.

Garnets

The garnet is invariably associated with a gem stone of dark red color. Actually, garnets occur in many different shades, and there are at least five varieties. Their chemical compositions are complicated and varied, but all consist of a double silicate in which one of the metals may be calcium, ferrous iron, magnesium, or manganese, and the other, aluminum, ferric iron, or chromium.

Perhaps the best known of all garnets is the pyrope variety, a magnesium aluminum silicate with a composition that can be expressed as $Mg_3Al_2(SiO_4)_3$. An important point to note is that the varieties are not sharply separated, but grade into one another. This means that one type may contain varying amounts of metals of another, so that the chemical composition is never constant. The name pyrope originates from the Greek word *pyr,* meaning fire. This particular garnet was popular in Victorian days, and much jewelry of this period is set almost entirely with deep-red stones.

A similarity to the color of ruby has led to a considerable amount of misnaming of the pyrope garnet. Pyropes occurring in association with diamonds in South Africa have been called "Cape rubies," while pyrope pebbles from Arizona and New Mexico have been sold locally as "Arizona rubies." Many of these stones are also found in Czechoslovakia, where they are known as Bohemian garnets.

A close relative of the pyrope is the almandine garnet. Here, iron replaces the magnesium in the chemical formula $Fe_3Al_2(SiO_4)_3$. Pyrope and almandine, however, are not sharply defined varieties, and it is quite possible that neither of them can be found in nature in the absolutely pure form. Almandine is a red stone and generally has a purplish tinge. Because of its very dark color, little light is allowed to penetrate. These stones are normally cabochon cut, and, because of their deep color, this is often modified into a rounded shell, called hollow cabochon, so as to present only a thin layer of the stone to the eye. Almandine garnets are chiefly found in the gem gravels of Ceylon and in India, where many of them are cut and marketed. At present, these stones are of limited popularity and are rarely seen in modern jewelry.

The so-called rhodolite garnet has the rose-red color of certain rhododendrons. It belongs to the pyrope-almandine intermediate series of garnets. Rhodolite garnets have been found in North Carolina, but stones of similar color have also been discovered in the Ceylon gem gravels and Tanzania.

Another type is the grossularite garnet, of which the hessonite is a variety. Both are calcium aluminum silicates, $Ca_3Al_2(SiO_4)_3$ with the metals iron and manganese sometimes partly replacing the calcium. Hessonite garnet is the color of golden syrup and is mainly found as pebbles in the gem gravels of Ceylon. Grossularite garnet occurs in massive green chunks, and is found in South Africa where it is known as "Transvaal jade."

Then there is the demantoid garnet, a variety of andradite, and a gem stone of exceptional beauty. Chemically, it is a calcium iron silicate, $Ca_3Fe_2(SiO_4)_3$. The best stones are of fine, grass-green color. Cut as gems, they equal the diamond in their brilliance, but their fire is not so well seen, being hidden by the green color of the stone. Demantoids are known to occur only in the Ural Mountains, and, unfortunately, this source seems now to be exhausted.

Like the diamond, all garnets belong to the cubic crystal system. Most of them possess a hardness of about 7¼, an exception being demantoid, with 6½. Apart from their uses in jewelry, garnets are employed as an abrasive, primarily for the polishing of wood.

Turquoise

The turquoise has remained almost unrivaled in its popularity throughout the centuries. Five thousand years ago the Egyptians mined these attractive blue and green stones in the Sinai Peninsula and then set them in varied mosaics and jewelry. Although these ancient mines are still partially worked today, the principal source of the finest deep-blue stones is in the Khorasan province of Iran.

Chemically, turquoise is a complex phosphate of aluminum with a hardness of 6 on the Mohs scale. Its blue color, which makes it so attractive, is due to the presence of a copper compound. Small individual crystals are extremely rare, some having been found in the United States, but the bulk of this mineral is found in masses composed of innumerable tiny crystal grains. It is thus cryptocrystalline in composition.

In earlier days, faultless stones of a single blue color were most valued, but today, because pure turquoise is almost unavailable, the so-called turquoise matrix, which is turquoise interspersed with dark veins of limonite, is popular.

Because of its porosity, turquoise is sensitive to chemicals and should not be brought into contact with soaps and detergents. The color of some stones may fade if exposed to light for a long time, while specimens of a fine blue color may turn green.

Fossil bones and teeth of prehistoric animals colored blue or green by iron phosphate are occasionally unearthed. These fossil remains are known as odontolite, or bone turquoise, but their organic structure can easily be detected with a strong lens or by the use of a microscope.

Jade

The word "jade" brings to mind a green, opaque stone. Commercially, it is used to describe two distinct minerals. The first is nephrite, also known as "green stone." If examined under the microscope, it will show a structure of tiny monoclinic crystals well matted together into a tight mass. It is a tough mineral, despite its hardness of only 6½. Because nephrite is so tough, it was much used in ancient times for tools and implements, some of which have been discovered in Mexico and in the vicinity of lake dwellings in Switzerland.

The color of nephrite largely depends on the amount of iron oxide present in the mineral, and this may vary from near white through light to dark green. New Zealand is one of its chief sources of supply, and it has been

47. Jade objects excavated in southeastern Mexico

used for centuries by the Maori natives of the area to carve weapons, tools, and ornamental objects. Other sources are the Jordanów Slaski district in Silesia, Poland (formerly Jordansmühl, Germany), Central Asia, and North America, where deposits are located at Jade Mountain in northwestern Alaska. More recently, nephrite has also been found north of the Wind River Range of the Rocky Mountains.

Jadeite is the rarer and the more highly prized of the two jades. Chemically, it is a silicate of sodium and aluminum having the formula $NaAl(SiO_3)_2$. It consists of a mass of interlocking crystals of the monoclinic crystal system that are granular in nature and show slight differences in hardness. Jadeite is a tough mineral, with a hardness of 7, but owing to the before-mentioned hardness variations, its polished surface has a slightly dimpled effect. It occurs in a variety of lovely shades. White, gray, orange, and mauve stones have been found, but the more usual color is green. The finest variety of this color is emerald green, due to the presence of the metal chromium. Today, the best jadeite is still mined in Upper Burma, and most of the production is purchased by the Chinese, whose fine craftsmen carve the stones into ornaments and statues. Chinese craftsmen have worked a tough green mineral material in their workshops for well over a thousand years, and they called this Yü, but it could not have been the jadeite mined in Burma since this material did not enter China before the eighteenth century. The mineral the Chinese worked with before this time was probably nephrite, which they obtained from Central Asian deposits at Khotan.

48. Chinese jade cup (660–221 B.C.)

Green Zircon	Blue Zircon	Almandine Garnet	Demantoid Garnet
Turquoise	Nephrite		Moonstone
Jadeite	Chrysoberyl Cat's-eye	Star Sapphire	Star Ruby

These stones were illuminated from above by one photographic floodlight only, in order to produce the star effect in the star sapphire and star ruby. This caused prominent light reflection in some other stones

In the Western world, the jades are not counted among the so-called precious stones, such as the diamond, the ruby, and the emerald, and are mostly used for carved ornamental objects, although attractive jewelry is also designed from this material. On the other hand, in some countries of the East, in particular, in China, where jade has been treasured for centuries both for its beauty in the form of carved objects and for its ritual significance, this mineral ranks equal in esteem and value with the precious stones of our Western society. This is an example of how fashion and custom may determine the value of gems.

Peridot

This attractive green gem stone belongs to the olivine mineral family. At one end of this family is found a mineral named forsterite, a magnesium silicate, Mg_2SiO_4, at the other fayalite, an iron silicate with the formula Fe_2SiO_4. Peridot is chemically a magnesium iron silicate, $(MgFe)_2SiO_4$ and lies between the two. Peridot is one of the few gems that occur in nature in one color only. This is due to the metal iron, which forms part of its basic formula. We call such minerals *idiochromatic,* or "self-colored."

The finest peridots come from the Isle of St. John in the Red Sea, and other sources are Burma and Arizona. The most famous belongs to the U.S.S.R. and once formed part of the royal Russian regalia. This stone is said to be crystal clear and of a fine olive-green color, weighing slightly over 192 carats. Gem-quality peridots of this size are exceedingly rare.

Peridot has a hardness of 6½, but with care it can be worn for a long time without showing undue wear.

The Feldspar Group

The feldspars are an important group of rock-forming minerals and are widely distributed over the earth. Chemically, they are silicates of aluminum and another metal, which may be potassium, sodium, or calcium.

The milky-white shimmering moonstone so often met with in jewelry is the best known of the feldspar gems. It belongs to the orthoclase variety and is a potassium feldspar with a general formula $KAlSi_3O_8$. Chief sources of moonstone are the gem gravels of Ceylon and Burma. A yellow transparent orthoclase form is also found in the island of Madagascar. Yet another potassium feldspar with the same formula is the green opaque microline variety known as amazonite, found chiefly in Colorado and in the Ural Mountains. It is somewhat similar in appearance to poor quality turquoise.

The sodium and calcium varieties fall into the group known as plagioclase feldspars. Only two of these are of interest in jewelry: the gray variety, labradorite, which shows a metallic play of color at its cleavage surfaces, and a reddish spangled variety known as sunstone. The latter seems to derive its red glow from the light reflection of crystals of an iron mineral within its structure.

All feldspar gems have a hardness approximating 6 and are mostly used in cheaper jewelry.

In industry, feldspar minerals are of importance in the manufacture of porcelain and are a component of glazes on earthenware, enameled brick, and many other objects that are glazed before use.

Lapis Lazuli

The finest lapis lazuli is an opaque stone of a deep blue color. Paler tints are also common, and some stones contain glistening spangles of iron pyrites. Lapis has a variable composition and is really a mixture of different rock-forming minerals, hauynite, lazurite, sodalite, and others; occasionally the golden iron pyrites may also be present. The chief source of the best lapis lazuli is in the Badakhshan area of Afghanistan. Inferior material is also found at Lake Baikal in Siberia and in Chile.

Sphene

Sphene is the silicate and titanate of calcium, and its chemical formula is $CaTiSiO_5$. One of the less-known and rarer gem stones, it occurs in yellow, green, and brown shades. Despite its hardness of only 5½, its truly exciting fire, which exceeds that of the diamond, makes it a valuable and much-desired gem. Sphene rarely occurs in gem-quality crystals, and those that have been found come chiefly from Austria, Switzerland, Mexico, and Brazil.

Spodumene

Spodumene is a silicate of lithium and aluminum, with a chemical formula LiAl $(SiO_3)_2$. Only two forms are cut as gem stones, the emerald-green and very rare variety hiddenite, and the lilac-and-pink variety known as kunzite. These stones should be handled with great care since they are brittle and if dropped may develop flaws.

Chief sources for kunzite are California, Brazil, and Madagascar. Hiddenite used to be found in North Carolina but sources are now exhausted.

This mineral has a hardness of 6½–7 and with reasonable care can be used as a ring stone.

Fluorspar

This mineral is calcium fluoride with the chemical composition CaF_2. It occurs in nature in violet, blue, purple, green, yellow, brown, and pink cubic crystals. The best known gem form is the purple-and-white banded variety known as "Blue John," which was much in demand for carved objects and vases. Its only source used to be in Derbyshire, England, before supplies became exhausted.

Fluorspar also has many industrial uses. The transparent mineral is used in making lenses, and other pure forms find uses in the manufacture of opalescent glasses and hydrofluoric acid. It has a hardness of only 4, too soft to retain a high polish, and thus is unsuitable as a ring stone.

V ORGANIC GEMS

Pearls

Unlike a gem stone, the pearl is an organic product of nature. It combines beauty with rarity and is highly prized in the world of jewels.

Natural pearls are obtained from shellfish, though it must not be taken for granted that all shellfish produce pearls. Only two groups, the pearl oysters and the pearl mussels, normally give us these gems. The pearl oysters live in the sea, while the pearl mussels are found in rivers and streams. It is wishful thinking to hope to find a pearl in an edible oyster, because only very rarely are pearls found in them, and even then they are far too tiny and too lusterless to be of value.

Pearl oysters occur in the southern oceans of the world and thrive best in a temperature of about 25° centigrade. They congregate in vast numbers attached to rock banks in the more shallow waters. Rarely are they found below a depth of about 30 feet. One of the most productive pearl areas in the world is the Persian Gulf, and the pearl industry there is carried on from many thousands of primitive small fishing boats, and not, as might be

49. Pearl fisher in the Persian Gulf

imagined by some, from modern motor boats. Each boat is manned by a small crew and a diver. Usually these divers work with only a rope and a knife, the rope being used as a life line to help the diver to surface with his load of shells. These he collects in a net or basket tied around his waist by a stout leather belt. The knife is his only protection against possible attacks by sharks. A diver can remain under water for about 2 minutes, and during this time he has to collect as many shells as possible. The diver's life is often in danger. In Australia, however, pearl divers do not face the same risks because they wear proper diving equipment.

Pearls are of different colors. Indeed, there are many shades, depending upon the locality where they were fished. For example, pearls from the Persian Gulf have a delicate creamy sheen, while on the coast of Western Australia there is an area known as Shark Bay, where the oysters yield yellowish pearls. Then again, in the Gulf of California or the Gulf of Mexico, some black pearls with a rich metallic luster are found. Nobody really knows what determines the color of pearls, except that it is known that their shade is caused by the nature of the water in which the oysters live, by the species, and by the location in the animal where the pearl has grown. Just by looking at the color of a pearl an expert can usually tell from which part of the world it came.

On the other hand, pearls that come from fresh-water mussels used to be much sought after at one time. Today, most pearl-mussel seekers are usually amateurs who search for the fun of it. It would not be worth it to a professional to search for them.

There are some rivers in the United States as well as abroad where the pearl mussel is to be found, and if one cares to provide himself with high boots, a forked stick, and a drum with a glass bottom, he might yet find a real pearl. The drum with the glass bottom enables one to see the river bed, and the forked stick will dislodge the shells. Apart from these simple gadgets, the hunt will require a great deal of patience, for few shells will contain pearls and fewer still will have that appearance that makes them so attractive and therefore valuable.

The question is, how can a simple creature like a mussel produce such a beautiful object? The animal itself lives between two shells (called *valves*) that are this soft and defenseless creature's only protection against the many hazards it meets in the rivers. Like ourselves, these animals must breathe, and this they do through gills in a way similar to fish. That means they pass water through the gills and in doing so extract oxygen from the water. Attached to the gills are tiny hairs called *cilia* that are in constant motion. These set up a continuous current of water that enters a small

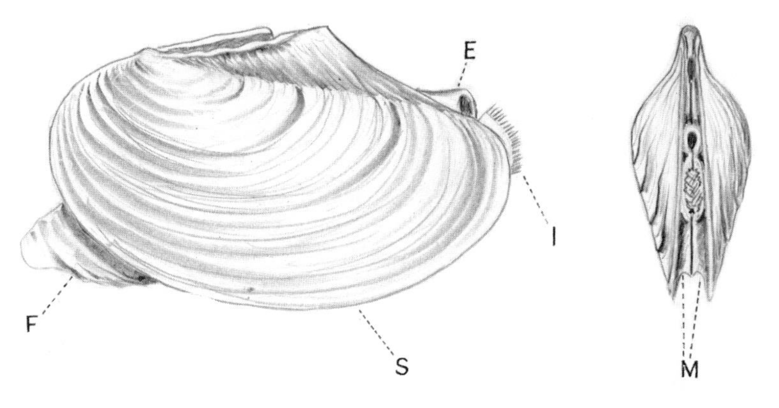

50. The swan-mussel: F is the foot, S, shell, I, inhalant siphon, E, exhalant siphon, M, mantle

opening, the *inhalant siphon* (Fig. 50). The ingoing current of water carries with it not only oxygen for breathing, but also many microscopic organisms are swept into the mouth by the action of the cilia, so mussels can both feed and breathe in one efficient operation.

The mussel also possesses an organ looking like a tongue that protrudes between the shell valves. This is called a *foot.* By means of its foot, the mussel is able to plow its way through sand and mud. Normally, when the animal is at rest, the two shell valves are opened so that it can breathe, feed, and expel waste materials. When the mussel is attacked, it quickly withdraws its foot, and the two shell valves close tightly. In this position, it is practically safe from its enemies.

If the shell of an oyster or mussel is cut through vertically and placed under the microscope, it would look something like a sandwich (Fig. 51).

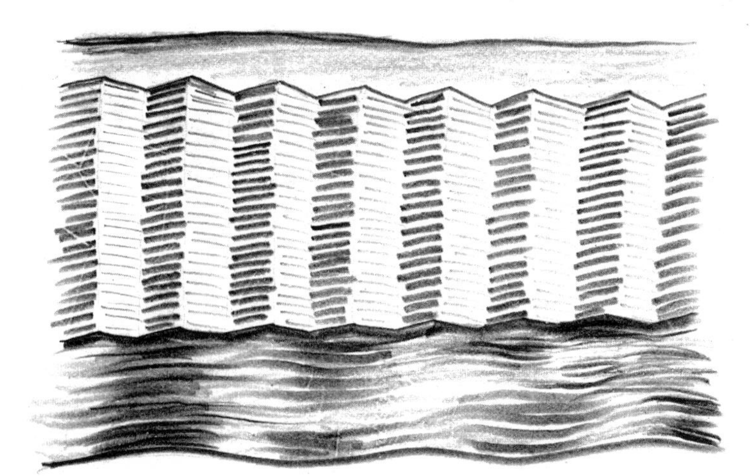

51. Drawing of a vertical section of the shell of a pearl mussel

First, there would be a hard, horny outer layer. This is part of the shell that is in contact with the outside and is called the *periostracum.* It is made from the material *conchiolin.* Next comes a thicker layer, called the *prismatic layer,* which consists of minute regular crystals of calcium carbonate, all of which lie in the same direction, at right angles to the shell. Finally, the shells are lined by a substance called nacre, better known as mother-of-

52. Drawing of the surface structure of a pearl under high magnification, showing zigzag lines which are the exposed edges of plates of calcium carbonate

pearl. This layer is made up of tiny plates of calcium carbonate that overlap one another rather like slates on a roof. Their edges are zigzagged and irregular and are so close together that they can be seen only under the microscope (Fig. 52). It is this last layer that gives the inside of oyster or mussel shell its iridescent luster.

All the parts of the shell are produced by the oyster that lives inside it, and this is accomplished in the following way. The body of the oyster is contained in two flaps of tissue, the *mantle.* This mantle is covered with minute cells, which have the power to pour out shell-forming substances. The outer horny layer and thicker prismatic layer are normally produced by the edge of the mantle only, and the layer of mother-of-pearl is secreted from cells of the whole mantle surface.

A pearl is formed in a very similar way. Imagine, for example, that a grain of sand or a minute worm gets into the shell and begins to irritate the soft body of the animal. Obviously, the oyster or mussel will first endeavor to expel it. Failing this, the only other alternative is to cover the foreign matter with layers of smooth shell material so as to allay any irritation. The same mantle that normally secretes substances to form the shell will now begin to deal with the intruding sand grain by secreting around it layer after layer of horny organic material and calcium carbonate. Many hundreds of such layers will be secreted around the sand grain until, over a long period of time, a pearl is formed. Each layer of organic material is minutely thin and cannot be seen without high magnification. It consists of a delicate network of cells, rather like a honeycomb, made from the horny substance, conchiolin, and these cells are filled with minute crystals of calcium carbonate.

Why a pearl shines can be explained by examining the pearl's surface under the microscope. There it will look like a large, silver-white dome crossed by the same zigzag lines as on the insides of the shells. Those zigzag lines are the exposed edges of tiny plates of calcium carbonate that overlap one another and form the mother-of-pearl layer. The behavior of light and how it travels along in the form of minute waves was discussed earlier. Red light waves are the longest, and, passing from the red to the yellow and green to the violet, the waves become shorter and shorter. In the ordinary way, all these waves stay together, and their combined effect on the eye is that of ordinary white sunlight. But if light strikes the surface of a very thin transparent film like the wall of a soap bubble or the thin transparent plates on the surface of the pearl, things begin to alter; some of the waves will interfere with one another. A red wave may reinforce another one of its kind and increase its intensity, while, conversely, two blue waves may mutually destroy one another, and darkness results. This phenomenon is called *interference,* and it explains the many shimmering colors on soap bubbles and also the iridescent luster of pearls. The luster of the mother-of-pearl lining on the inside of the shells is also caused by the same phenomenon.

As with other precious gems, man has for centuries endeavored to find ways and means of producing pearls artificially. Unlike some gem stones, pearls cannot be synthesized, but man has found an ingenious way of culturing them.

Cultured pearls are usually associated with Japan, but it was the Chinese who, nearly five hundred years ago, discovered the fact that if a foreign object were introduced between the shell and the mantle of a fresh-water pearl mussel, that object would eventually become coated with a layer of mother-of-pearl. Sometimes the Chinese inserted small stones, a splinter of

53. Pearl oysters (*Pinctada martensi*). One has been opened, revealing a cultured pearl

wood, or even the image of a Buddha cast in metal. The mussel was then returned to the river and allowed to live there for a few years. When it was fished up and opened, the foreign object had become coated with mother-of-pearl and was fixed to the shell.

Over the centuries, many have tried to improve on these ancient methods, but it was not until the early part of this century that the Japanese made enormous improvements in the technique of forcing shellfish to produce pearls. The resulting products are today known as cultured pearls.

In Japanese waters, there are several species of shellfish that produce natural pearls, but only a few of these can be used as "mother shells" for cultured pearls. The one most commonly selected for culturing operations is the akoya oyster, or *Pinctada martensi* (see Fig. 53). It is one of the most hardy of the species and stands up well to the rather harsh treatment of the culturing operation.

To satisfy world demand for cultured pearls, a large number of healthy pearl oysters are needed, because only really strong and healthy specimens can produce the best gems. This means that they have to be specially bred, and for this purpose many thousands of young oysters have to be collected.

In the months of June and July in the waters around Japan, each mother oyster is said to produce one hundred to two hundred thousand young, and, since there are many millions of mother oysters in the waters, each year astronomical numbers of young oysters will be produced. Not all of these will survive. The majority will be killed by natural enemies, such as the starfish and the octopus, and many will be carried far out into the ocean and die there. The first task of the cultivator, then, is to find some method whereby the young oyster larvae can be readily collected. Collectors, consisting of twigs taken from the Japanese cedar tree, are cut into 2- or 3-foot lengths, then tied together. Sometimes, old fishing nets with fine meshes are used. When the spawning season arrives, the collectors are hung in the water from rafts, and the oyster larvae attach themselves to these. The larvae are allowed to grow on the collectors until they are about the size of a fingernail. Then they are taken from the collectors and placed into fine-mesh wire baskets. As the young oysters grow, they are removed into new baskets with larger mesh, and their numbers are, at the same time, decreased.

There are some difficulties to overcome, however. Oysters are cold-blooded creatures and cannot adapt themselves to changes in the temperature of the sea water. If the water is either too cold or too hot, the oysters may weaken and die. As the cold season approaches, they must be removed to winter quarters where the temperature of the sea water does not fall below 10° centigrade. There, they grow up for a period of 2 to 3 years until they reach maturity and are ready for the culturing operation. When the oysters are mature, they are removed from the sea, and some of them are opened, and small squares of healthy mantle tissue removed. These oysters are then discarded. The operator now wedges open the remaining oysters and makes an incision into their mantle tissues. He next takes a mother-of-pearl bead, together with a square of previously prepared mantle tissue, and inserts it into the incision (Fig. 54). After this operation, the oysters are put in wire baskets and returned to a quiet part of the sea.

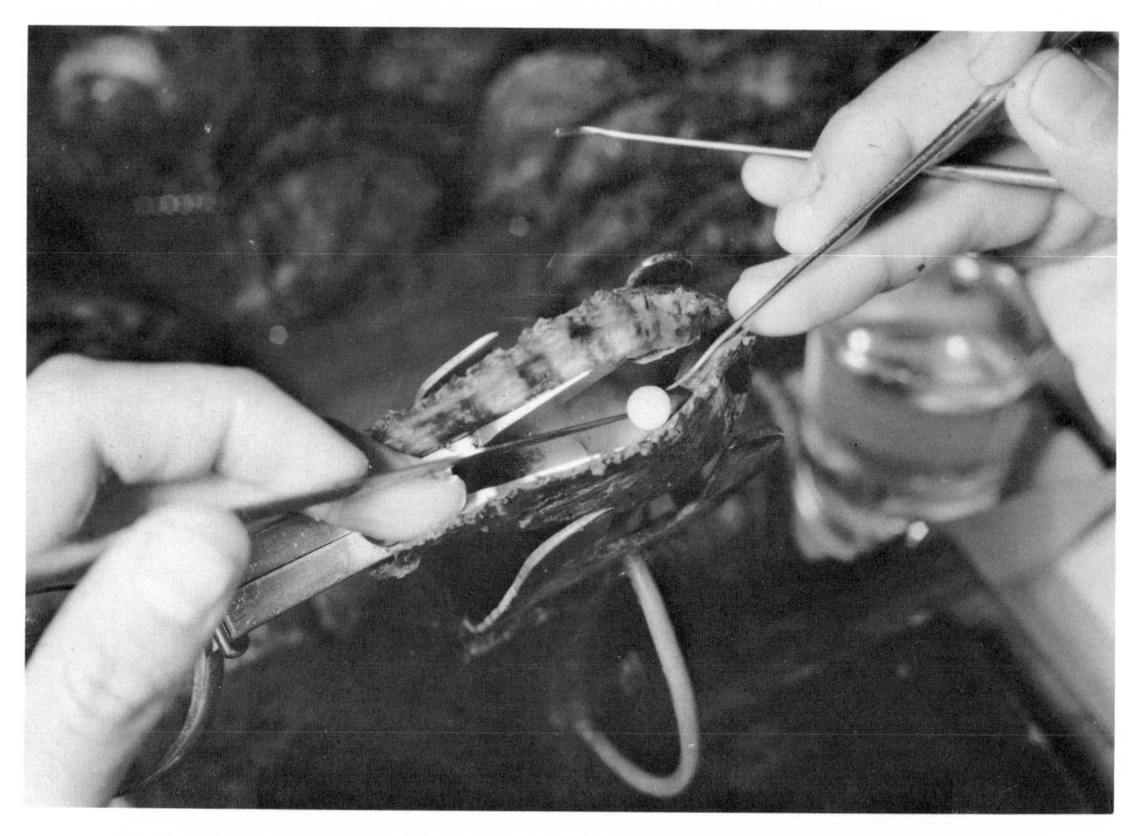

54. Inserting a mother-of-pearl nucleus into the mother oyster, which is held open with a wedge

After a period of rest and recuperation, they are placed in wire baskets in groups of 20 to 40 per basket and taken to the cultivation farms where they hang from rafts into the sea. At this stage, cultivation proper commences.

The oyster, as has been said, is able to render intruders into its shell harmless by surrounding them with layer upon layer of calcium carbonate, and this is what takes place now. Slowly, the mother-of-pearl bead is surrounded by layer upon layer of fresh mother-of-pearl substance. Cultivation may take any time from one year for small pearls to 4 years for really large

55. Women divers sometimes take mother oysters from the bottom of the sea. Mostly, however, they are cultivated in fine-meshed metal baskets hung from rafts

ones. Four or five times a year, the outer shells and baskets have to be cleaned and freed from other small sea creatures that may have become attached to them. In addition, they must be able to obtain food. This consists mainly of minute animal or vegetable plankton, and the oyster rafts

56. Oysters are sometimes fastened to ropes during the cultivation process

57. A typical pearl farm with clusters of rafts floating on calm water in inlets and bays. Thousands of mother pearls are contained in the baskets hung from the rafts

58. Oyster rafts being attended by Japanese workers

must be placed in the correct positions to enable the tidal flows to supply them with enough food. Oysters are, in fact, quite fussy customers, since a too plentiful supply of food can be bad for them.

When all has gone well, and the pearls are ready for harvesting, the oysters are fished up again during the winter months when the secretion of the mother-of-pearl substance is at a minimum. At this time the oysters are killed, and the pearls are extracted and cleaned. Tremendous wastage

59. Grading and sorting cultured pearls

is unavoidable. Only about 85 per cent of the one-year oysters and 45 per cent of the 4-year oysters will have produced successful pearls, while a mere 5 per cent will be found to be absolutely faultless.

Cultured pearls are not as valuable as natural ones, but a good deal will depend on the quality of both. Recently, some magnificent cultured pearls

60. Grading cultured pearls for necklaces

have been produced, some of which are said to be as big as hazel nuts, and these are indeed valuable.

But do not imagine that producing cultured pearls on a big scale is an easy task. There are hazards. Typhoons, which frequently sweep the coastal waters of Japan, can cause millions of dollars worth of damage. High winds and gigantic waves may destroy and scatter the rafts so that many oysters are killed or lost. Heavy prolonged rain may swell the rivers running to the sea and reduce the saline content of the sea water near the oyster farms. This will kill many of the oysters. Luckily, river water flows above the sea water, and, by suspending the baskets close to the bottom of the sea, some of this hazard can be minimized.

Few people realize that pearls must be treated with care to allow them to retain their full beauty. They are of organic origin and therefore may deteriorate under certain conditions, but, naturally, much will depend on how carefully they are kept. The pearls that hang from the arches of the English State Crown have retained their luster after nearly 400 years.

As with most precious gems, there have also been famous pearls. The giant of them all measured nearly 2 inches at its longest, had a circumference of almost 4 inches, and weighed about 3 ounces. But the most beautiful pearl known in history was named "La Pellegrina." It was said to have originated in the Indian Ocean. In perfection of shape it outshone all competitors. It was white in color, symmetrical and pear-shaped, and weighed 111 pearl grains. The *pearl grain* is equal to ¼ carat.

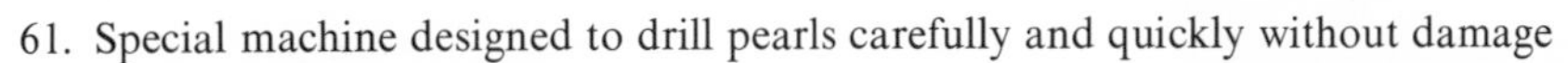

61. Special machine designed to drill pearls carefully and quickly without damage

The natural combination known as the great Southern Cross is famous. This consists of nine pearls naturally united in the form of a cross. It was discovered in the 1880's in a pearl oyster fished off the coast of Western Australia.

The pink, or conch pearls, produced by the univalve *Strombus gigas* are of commercial importance. Pink or white in color, these pearls have a porcelainlike appearance, somewhat similar to coral. Under a lens they show flamelike markings, which distinguish them from coral.

Amber

Amber is not a gem stone but an organic substance of vegetable origin. It consists of the fossilized resin of coniferous trees long since extinct. It is found in a range of shades from clear yellow to a very deep yellow. Each one of the shades can be modified by the inclusion of many fine air bubbles, which give the amber a cloudy appearance. "Amber" which is very bright red, greenish, or completely black, is fossilized tree gum of lesser age.

One of its most fascinating aspects is its extreme age, the true ambers having originated in the Oligocene period some forty to fifty million years ago. In these prehistoric times, large quantities of sticky resins oozed from the timbers of coniferous trees, trapping in the process many kinds of insects, beetles, butterflies, and even small lizards. Today, these animals can still be seen encased in chunks of amber almost as if all this had happened yesterday instead of millions of years ago. Many of these varied animal and plant inclusions are, of course, immensely valuable to scientific research, for they give a very clear picture of certain aspects of life in those early times. A fine collection of animal and plant inclusions was formerly housed in the amber museum at Königsberg, East Prussia (now Kaliningrad in Russia). During the siege of 1944, the collection was destroyed by fire.

As a gem, amber's attraction lies chiefly in its coloring. Its hardness is only 2½, and it is usually turned into rounded beads for necklaces or brooches where the risk of undue wear is minimized.

Until about the middle of the nineteenth century, all amber was recovered on the Baltic seashore where it was gathered in when the tide was low. Later, large underground deposits of it were discovered near the same shore, and today most of the amber is obtained by open-cast mining 40 miles west of Kaliningrad. Less important sources are Rumania, where small deposits of an inferior quality are found, and Burma, where ambers of a large variety of shades ranging from honey yellow to deep red are located.

Amberlike material is also washed up on the shores of Sicily. This Sicilian "amber" is highly thought of because of its rich, dark color, which sometimes exhibits a blue-green fluorescence.

Amber is fairly easy to imitate by means of various forms of plastic materials. If tested with a knife, however, true amber is found to chip, while the plastic imitations peel. Glass beads of the correct color have been used as imitations, but glass is considerably more dense than amber, and the weight difference immediately becomes apparent. Glass is colder to the touch, too, and its different luster is easily recognized.

Coral

The coral polyp belongs to a low form of life inhabiting the warmer oceans of the world. Its branching colonies may grow into enormous structures, such as the Great Barrier Reef off the east coast of Australia. The rose-colored or red coral, well known in cheaper jewelry, is chiefly found in the Mediterranean Sea and originates from the coral polyp *Corallium rubrum.* The animal multiplies by budding and splitting, and each division grows into a perfect new polyp consisting of a mass of jelly provided with numerous tentacles. It spends its life attached to submerged rocks and deposits a hard skeleton of calcium carbonate around the outer part of its body. Only this hard skeleton remains when the animal dies, and it is this skeleton that is known as coral.

The coral-fishing industry is now almost entirely confined to Italy and Japan, and most of its produce is exported to countries of the East.

VI THE DIAMOND CUTTERS

Diamond crystals, in their natural state, normally look as dull and uninteresting as pieces of ordinary washing soda. It is only the skill and craftsmanship of the diamond cutter that reveals their inherent beauty. Other gem minerals, too, must be cut and polished before they can be used in jewelry, but here an important distinction must be made. The cutting and polishing of gem stones is grouped under two distinct headings: (1) the cutting and polishing of diamonds, and (2) the cutting and polishing of all other gem materials. Those who cut diamonds are called diamond cutters, while those who cut and polish other types of gems are known as lapidaries.

The explanation of this distinction is simple. Because of the extreme hardness of diamonds, certain problems concerning the method of cutting and polishing arise that are not encountered when cutting and polishing other gems. Since diamond is the hardest known mineral on earth, how can the cutting and polishing of such an unyielding object be achieved? A fact-finding tour of the works of a progressive diamond cutter will reveal more about this highly technical subject.

Gem diamonds usually occur in nature in the crystal shape of a double pyramid, or octahedron, but such crystals are often badly misshapen and show internal flaws. It is important, therefore, to decide whether a crystal is sufficiently faultless and of the correct size to be cut into a jewel stone and, if not, how best to split it to remove the faults that exist. This splitting operation is known as cleaving, and requires great skill and knowledge, for, should a diamond cleaver strike the stone in the wrong place, a diamond worth many thousands of dollars may be ruined.

62. A diamond being sawed

It is possible to cleave a diamond, in spite of its extreme hardness, because diamond crystals can be split in the four planes parallel to the crystal faces of the octahedron. This is one of their directional properties.

Once the diamond cleaver has ascertained the direction in which the crystal is to be cleaved, it is cemented to the end of a wooden holder, and a smaller diamond is used to scratch a groove in it. A heavy steel blade is now placed in this groove in the correct position, and smartly struck. If the operation has been correctly carried out, the stone will split across exactly in the desired direction. Except in the case of large stones, this cleaving operation is not very often employed, and diamond sawing is usually the first process.

The sawing department may consist of a spacious room around the walls of which are arranged stout benches fitted with a multitude of diamond saws. One question that immediately arises is how it is possible to cut through a diamond, which is the hardest natural substance on earth, with a saw. Actually, saws, in the accepted sense, are not used: instead the

63. Mounting a roughly shaped diamond into a solder dop

diamond cutter uses extremely thin phosphor-bronze disks 1/300 inch thick, the edges of which are charged with a mixture of diamond dust and oil.

The diamond saws are under the care of a skilled foreman who watches carefully over the whirling disks, which spin at the phenomenal speed of 6,000 revolutions per minute. During the sawing operation, the diamond crystals are secured in special holders by means of clamps or set in plaster of Paris, and, unlike most other sawing operations, they rest on top of the whirling sawblades. Great care has to be taken in deciding in which direction a diamond shall be sawed, since there are certain directions in every stone that are so hard that even these specialized saws could not accomplish their task.

The time required for sawing a diamond may vary from a few hours to as long as several days, depending upon the size of the stone. Once a stone has been sawed to the correct size, it is taken to another department for an operation called *bruting*. This means shaping the actual stone to round it. At one time, two stones of similar size were selected, each being firmly embedded in suitable hollows already prepared in the ends of two wooden holders, leaving exposed only the parts to be shaped. One holder was held in each hand and the stones rubbed hard together against each other until both were shaped as required. This operation seems onerous, but today modern machinery has greatly eased the task of bruting.

The diamond is cemented into a cup-shaped object called a *dop* which is then screwed to the end of a metal shaft attached to a turning lathe. Another stone is mounted in another dop screwed to the end of a metal rod. The bruter now firmly grips the rod and rests it near the dop against a firm vertical support fixed to the bench. The lathe is now set in motion, and as the two stones are pressed against each other, rotates at about 400 revolutions per minute. In this way, the bruter brings considerable pressure to bear between the two diamonds, but great care must be exercised in the course of this operation in order to prevent overheating. The resulting diamond dust is carefully collected for future use in the sawing and polishing operations.

The bruting completed, the diamonds are now taken to the cutting and

64. The dop is applied to the revolving surface of the polishing lap

polishing shop, where a number of craftsmen are busy attending to machinery arranged on long wooden benches. Unlike other gem stones, diamonds are cut and polished in one operation, which is carried out on *polishing laps;* these are horizontal disks measuring about one foot in diameter and half an inch in thickness. These disks, composed of soft iron, spin at 2,500 revolutions per minute, and each lap is charged with a small amount of diamond dust mixed with olive oil. The diamonds are held in special dops similar to those used in the bruting operation. Since the heat developed by the friction between the fast rotating lap and the diamond is far too great to allow the gem to be held in position by ordinary cement, a special solder containing one part of tin to three parts of lead is employed. The dop containing the solder is placed into a gas flame and heated until it softens.

Once the solder has become pliable, the dop is removed with the aid of tongs and placed upright on a stand. Tongs are used to shape the solder into a cone at the apex of which the diamond is placed. The operator then proceeds to work the solder well over the stone so that it is firmly secured, with only the part to be polished exposed (see Fig. 63). Finally, in order to be cooled, the dop, with the stone in position, is plunged into water. Such

65. The diamond being polished in a mechanical dop

dramatic treatment would cause other gems to fly to pieces immediately, but not the diamond, which allows heat to be conducted away so quickly that even drastic temperature changes do not affect it in the least.

Once the diamond has been fixed in the appropriate manner in the dop, the copper stalk fixed to the bottom is fastened to the polishing arms resting over the polishing lap. The operation can now commence. Nowadays, much of this work is done with mechanical dops, the stone being gripped firmly by steel claws. This facilitates more accurate working and saves much time in resetting the stone.

Conventionally, diamonds are cut in the shape of the *brilliant cut,* each little facet on the crown and base being separately cut and polished onto the stone. There are 58 facets on a brilliant-cut diamond, so that the cutter

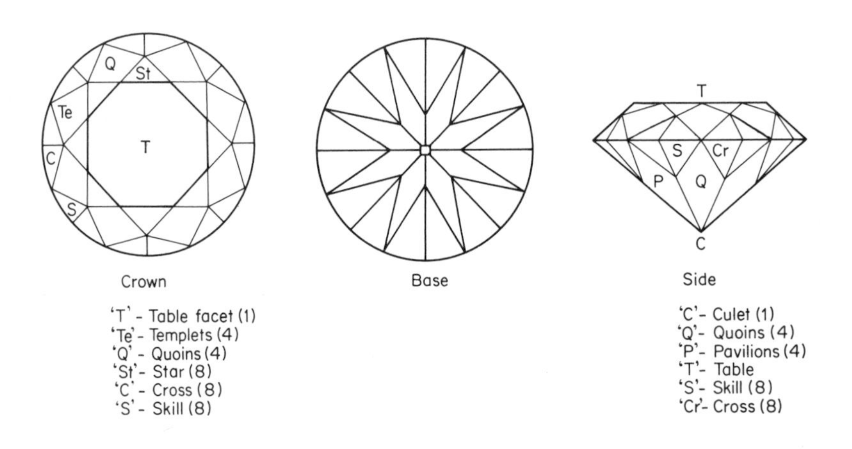

66. The brilliant cut

must reset the stone 58 times before his task is accomplished. Frequent inspection is necessary to insure that each facet has been cut and polished to the right degree.

Apart from cutting the conventionally shaped diamonds, A. Nagy, an English diamond cutter, has particularly distinguished his stones by the invention of the completely novel *profile cut.* This new shape, first shown publicly in 1961, took 13 years to perfect. It represents a completely new

67. The profile cut

Heart-shaped profile cut

Cross-section of profile cut

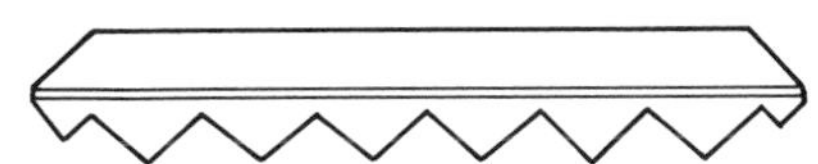

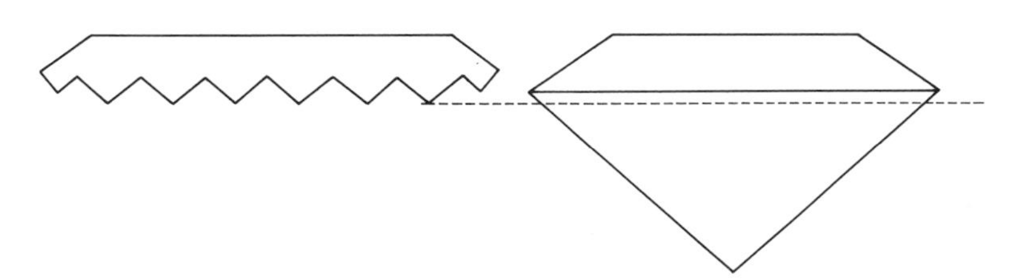

Total thickness of profile-cut diamond

Total thickness of brilliant-cut diamond

form of cutting and is the first innovation of its kind since the development of the brilliant cut.

Normally, for the conventional brilliant cut, an octahedral diamond crystal is sawed into halves, each producing a conventional brilliant-cut diamond. For the new profile cut, the same crystal is sawed into four plates, each of equal thickness. A specially adapted three-bladed saw disk is used for this operation. When cutting diamonds of any shape it is vitally important that the correct angles at which the facets should be set are achieved, otherwise the diamonds will lack the maximum fire and sparkle that makes them so attractive. If a diamond has been cut correctly, the same amount of light that enters the stone from the top should be totally reflected from the base facets, to be returned again through the top of the stone (Fig. 70).

When, finally, a stone has been cut and polished to the satisfaction of

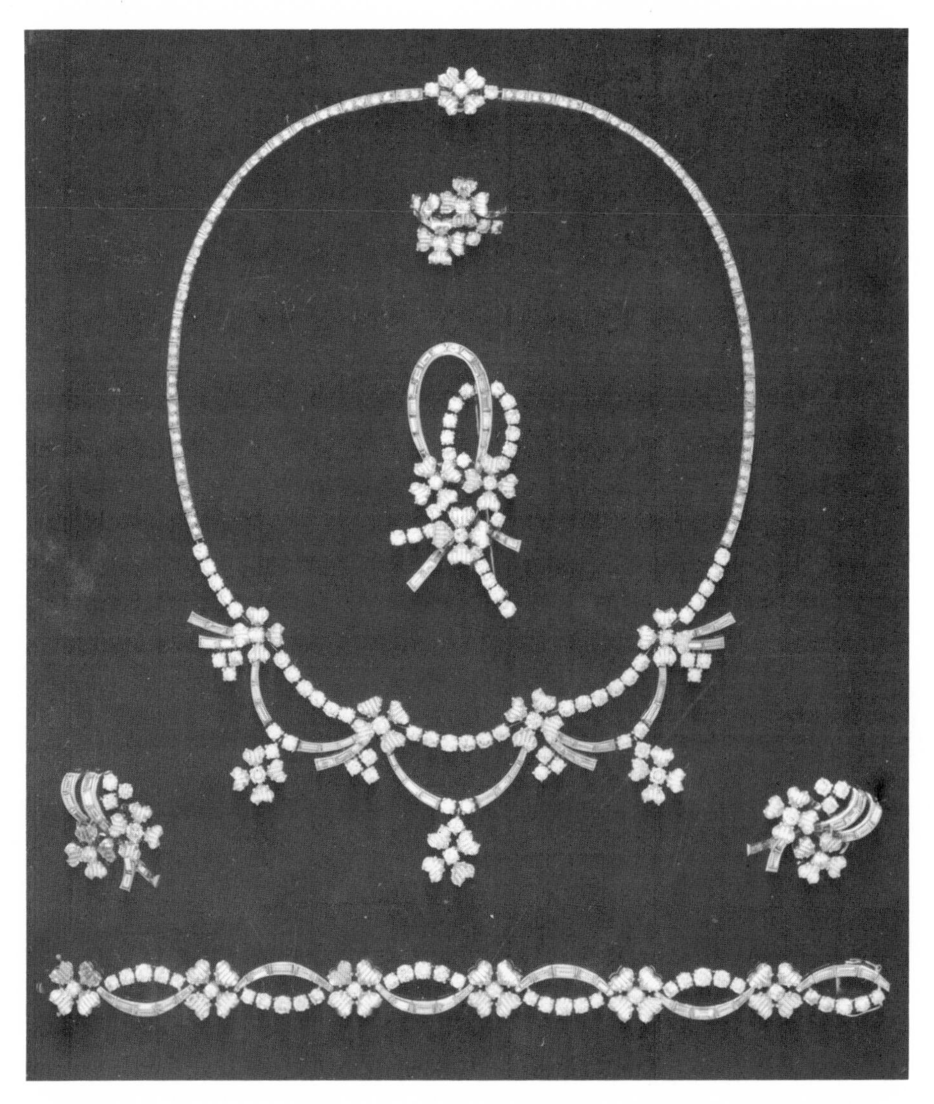

68. The first complete suite of jewelry designed in profile-cut diamonds. The heart-shaped stones, with their linear pattern, are easily distinguished from the conventionally cut stones

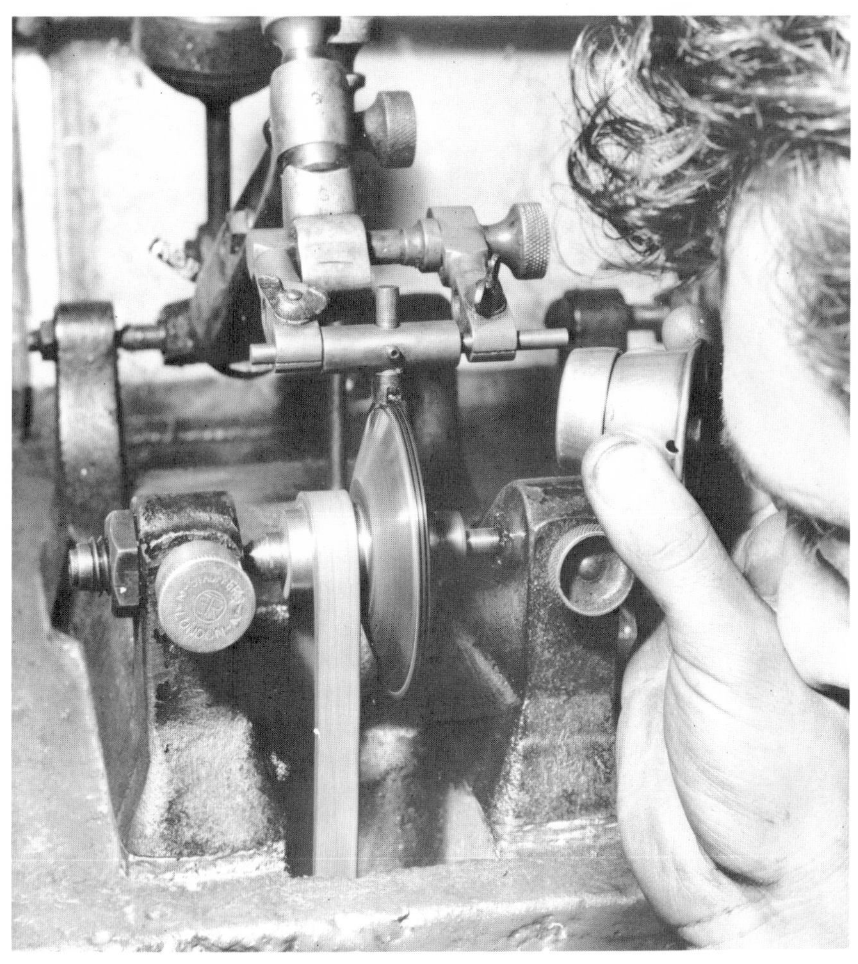

69. A diamond gang saw. This particular saw has three blades, used for the specialized profile cut

the craftsman, it is cleaned in boiling sulphuric acid to remove all traces of grease and dirt. This drastic treatment leaves the stone completely unharmed —once again illustrating its extreme resistance to all chemical influences.

The cutting and polishing of other gem stones is a relatively simple matter compared with that employed for diamond. None of them approach diamond in hardness, so that sawing is speedily accomplished by fast-rotating soft-metal wheels, the edges of which are charged with diamond

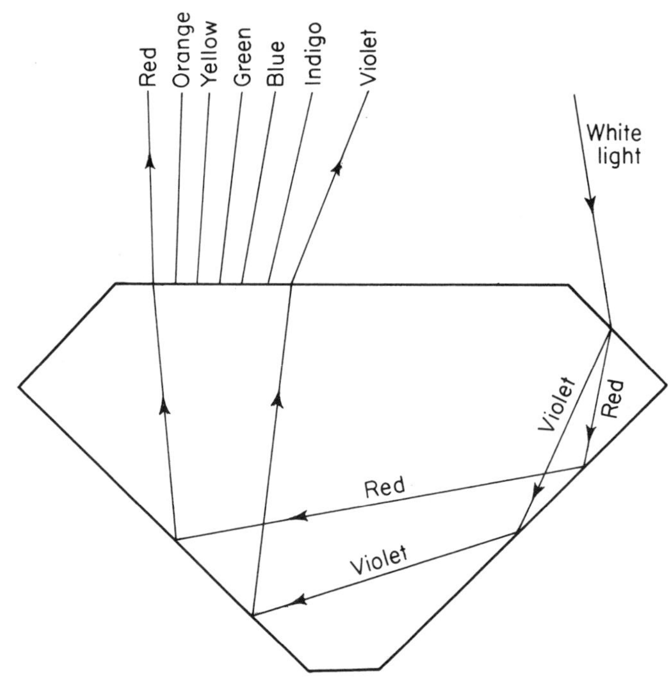

70. Dispersion of a ray of white light into its spectrum colors when passed through a brilliant-cut diamond

dust. There is no necessity to carry out the operation of bruting, described earlier. The grinding of the facets and their polishing is completed in two distinct operations. Grinding is done on metal laps charged with a suitable abrasive, such as diamond or carborundum powder, according to the hardness of the stone concerned. To carry out the polishing process, the cut stones are applied to wooden laps faced with leather or cloth to which a softer polishing agent has been applied. This removes all slight scratches and blemishes.

VII
TESTING GEMS

The previous chapters have dealt with the great variety of gems used in jewelry. Their economic value may vary enormously, depending on the particular type of gem, its quality, and whether it is of natural or synthetic origin. It will be seen that it is of the utmost importance for the whole of this vast industry that reliable methods for the identification of gems exist.

There is no simple formula by which gems can be identified and classified according to their worth, and even the most experienced jewel experts hesitate to give a firm opinion as to what a certain stone is, without first applying one, and preferably two, reliable tests. What are these tests, and how are they applied to gems?

Testing the Specific Gravity (Sp. G.)

Perhaps one of the most useful of all physical properties of minerals for testing purposes is their *specific gravity,* or relative density. This is not difficult to understand. Of two marbles, both of exactly the same size, but one made of wood and the other of steel, the latter will weigh considerably more than the former, so steel has a higher specific gravity than wood. To find the specific gravity of a gem stone, two methods are generally employed. Hydrostatic weighing is one, which will be investigated first, and the other is the use of heavy liquids.

71. General arrangement of a laboratory balance for the specific-gravity test

1. Construct a small wooden bridge and straddle it over the left balance pan, as shown in the photograph, so that the free swing of the balance remains unimpeded. (The bridge must, therefore, not touch the balance pan)
2. Place a glass beaker, three-quarters filled with boiled water, on the bridge. (Boiled or distilled water is necessary to remove any air.) The temperature of the water should be 4° centigrade
3. Make a spiral coil from a heavy-gauge copper wire, large enough to hold the mineral specimen. (A 30-ampere fuse wire is well suited)
4. Suspend the spiral coil by a fine wire from the lower hook of the balance arm into the beaker filled with water so that the specimen under test is well covered but does not touch the bottom of the beaker. (A 5-ampere household fuse wire is suitable as a suspension wire)
5. Place weights, or another piece of wire, into the second balance pan, to act as an exact counterpoise to the suspended wire and spiral coil
6. Take great care that no air bubbles cling to the wire or specimen before commencing the experiment. (Any bubbles can be removed with a fine paint brush.) Air bubbles can introduce an appreciable error into your results, because they act rather like a life jacket and tend to buoy up the wire and the specimen
7. Weigh the mineral specimen accurately to three decimal places in water
8. Weigh the mineral specimen accurately to three decimal places in air in the conventional way
9. Calculate results as described in text

Note: The weight of gem stones is always expressed in carats, but gram weights may be used

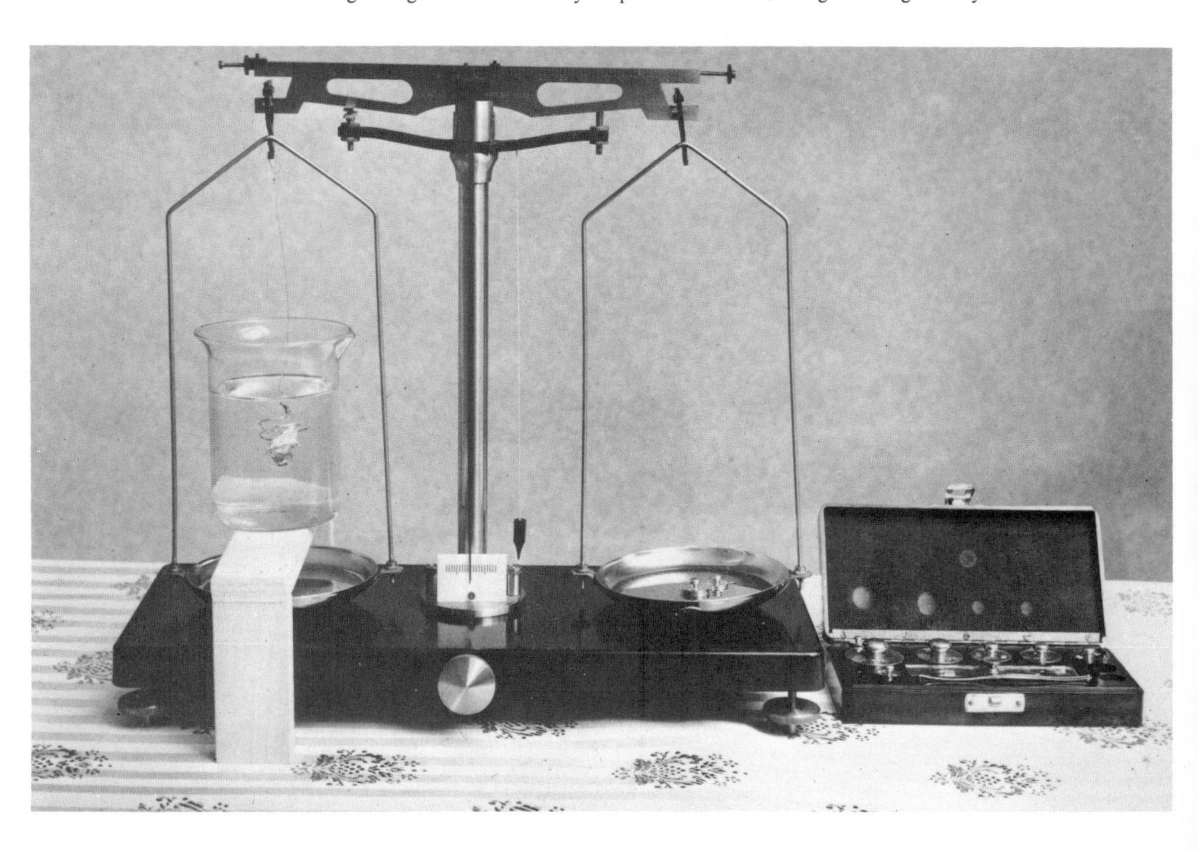

Diamond crystals

In the year 250 B.C., the Greek mathematician Archimedes studied this problem and discovered that when a body was immersed in a liquid it was buoyed up by it with a force equal to the weight of the displaced liquid. This is known as Archimedes' principle. It means that if a gem stone or mineral crystal is suspended in water, it will apparently suffer a loss in weight equal to the weight of water it displaces.

The specific gravity of a substance is defined as the ratio

$$\frac{\text{Weight of substance in air}}{\text{Weight of equal volume of water.}}$$

This may also be expressed as:

$$\frac{\text{Weight of substance in air}}{\text{Loss of weight in water.}}$$

Thus, by simply weighing a gem in air and then immersing it in water and weighing it again, all the data is available to calculate that gem stone's specific gravity.

Say one is asked to verify the identity of a large yellow stone that is supposed to be a valuable topaz. A stone of this color might also be the much less valuable yellow form of quartz (citrine). The tester proceeds as follows. First, he weighs the stone on an accurate laboratory scale and finds that it weighs 3 grams. He then weighs the same stone immersed in a tumbler of water. This is normally done by suspending the stone from the balance arm in a wire basket (see Fig. 71). That the gem has apparently lost some weight is obvious, for now it only weighs 1.87 grams. Applying the formula, the specific gravity of the stone will be:

$$\frac{\text{Weight in air} = 3 \text{ grams}}{\text{Loss of weight in water} = 1.13 \text{ grams}} = 2.65$$

Quartz has a specific gravity of 2.65, whereas topaz has a specific gravity of 3.53. The conclusion in this case can safely be that the stone is quartz, and not the more valuable topaz. In this way, mineral crystals and gems can be tested and identified effectively.

As mentioned, the second method of finding the specific gravity depends upon the use of heavy liquids. The principle is relatively simple since it is obvious that a stone will sink in a liquid less dense than itself and float in one that is denser. This result can be checked by putting a metal spoon in a tumbler of water and watching it sink. If a wooden spoon is put into the same tumbler, it will float. The reason, of course, is that the metal spoon is denser than water, and the wooden spoon less dense. If, therefore, a suitable range of heavy liquids of known densities can be obtained, stones under test can be placed into these liquids in order to observe whether they sink or rise to the surface. In this way, an approximate value of their densities can be arrived at.

There is a box of yellow stones to be sorted and all that is known about them is that they are a mixture of topaz and citrine. The value of the collection will depend on the proportion of either of the stones present, and the first task will be to separate them. The heavy liquids available for this purpose are bromoform, with a density of 2.9, and methylene iodide, density 3.33. Both can be diluted with suitable agents such as benzene or toluene to cover a wide range of intermediate densities.

Since the specific gravity of quartz is 2.65, and the denser topaz has a specific gravity of 3.53, a liquid between those two densities must be chosen so that the quartz will float and the topaz will sink. The most suitable in this case will be bromoform with a specific gravity of 2.9. If stones are dropped, one by one, into the liquid, all the less dense quartzes will float on the surface of the liquid, while the topaz will quickly sink to the bottom. In this way, the two types of gem stones can be quickly separated from each other. There are many variants to this method, which, if applied with skill, forms one of the most useful testing techniques.

Here a word of warning must be given. Many of the heavy liquids are either poisonous or give off harmful vapors. There are also some porous gem stones, such as the opal and turquoise, which would certainly be damaged if immersed in these liquids. These tests are therefore best left to the experienced operator. On the other hand, hydrostatic weighing can safely be applied to all gem materials and is a very useful practice for the beginner.

The Refractive Index and Its Measurement

Another quick and most reliable test on a gem stone is the measurement of its refractive index. Light travels through space at about 186,000 miles per second, but, as soon as it enters a denser medium such as a gem stone, its speed is lessened. In the diamond, the speed of light is reduced to 76,860 miles per second. The refractive index of a gem may be defined as the velocity of light in space divided by the velocity of light in the gem stone. In the case of diamond, this is:

$$\frac{186{,}000}{76{,}860} = 2.42.$$

It is, of course, far too complicated to measure the speed of light in a stone, and it was found that there is yet another ratio that will give the same results. The slowing down of the speed of light as it enters from air into a gem stone is also accompanied by the bending of the light rays. This bending process is called *refraction,* which was discussed earlier. The angle at which the light rays enter a gem is known as the *angle of incidence,* and the angle through which the ray is bent or refracted is known as the *angle of refraction* (see Fig. 17). If the *sine of the angle* of incidence is divided by the sine of the angle of refraction, the numerical value of the refractive

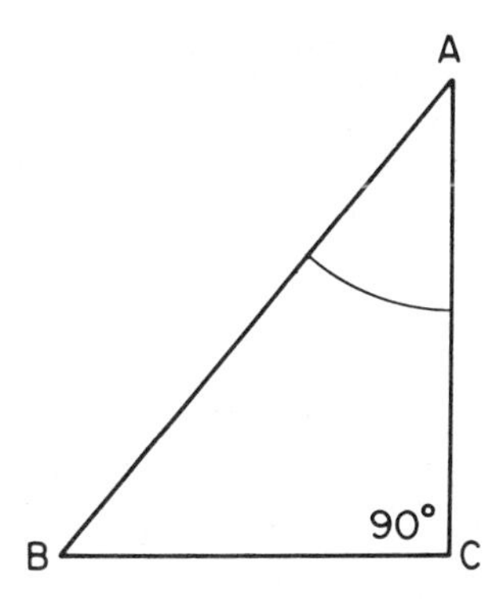

72. The sine of an angle

index is obtained. The sine of an angle is explained in Fig. 72; there the side *AB* of the right-angled triangle is opposite the right angle; it is called the hypotenuse. The sine of the angle *BAC* is the ratio of the side opposite the angle to the hypotenuse. In this case, side *BC* is opposite the angle *BAC*; therefore, sine angle $BAC = BC/AB$.

The problem of measuring these angles and arriving at the ratio was solved by the invention of the *refractometer,* an ingenious instrument which

73. Rayner refractometer, with gem stone in viewing position

enables one to read the refractive index of the stone directly on a calibrated scale. Simply expressed, one might say the greater the power of a gem stone to bend a light ray, the greater its refractive index. Or in terms of light speed, the greater the power of a gem to slow down the speed of light, the greater its refractive index.

All gem stones, except those belonging to the cubic crystal system, not only bend the light rays, but also split them in two (see Fig. 19). These two

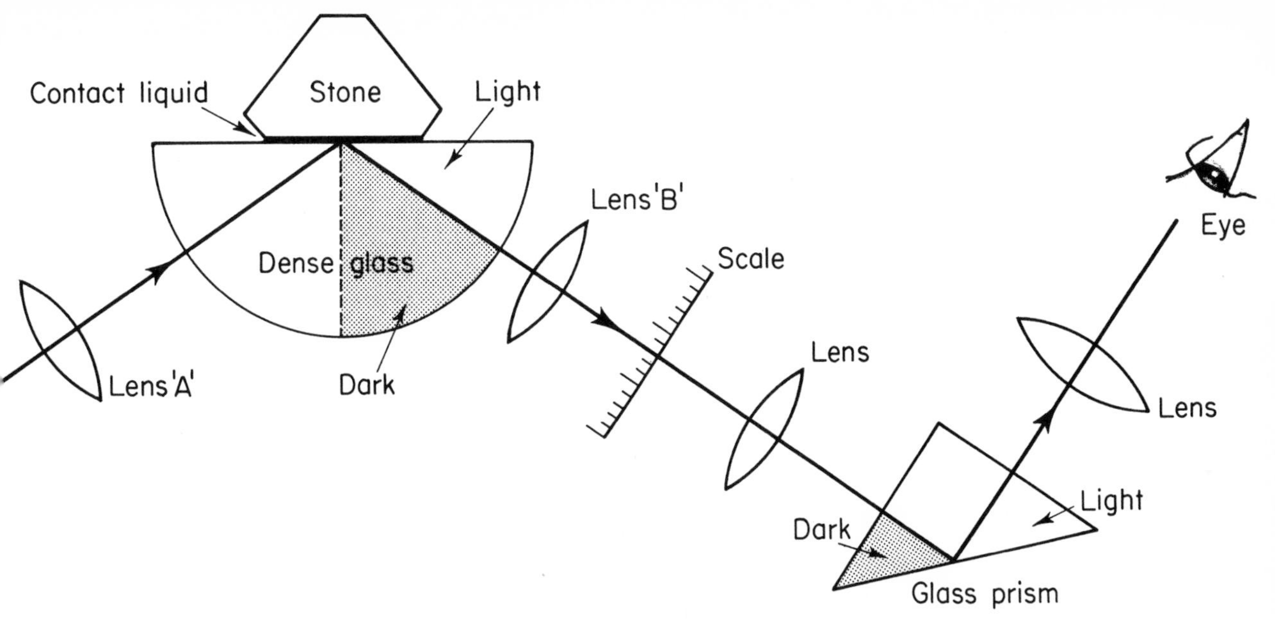

74. Diagram illustrating the working of the refractometer

The stone under test is in contact with a hemisphere, or prism, of optically very dense glass. The contact liquid between the stone and the glass insures perfect contact. Lens *A* admits light to the instrument, which passes into the dense glass. A portion of the light will be totally reflected at the surface dividing the gem stone under test and the glass. The totally reflected light passes through lens *B* on to a scale, part of which is brightly illuminated. The dark portion of the scale represents light not totally reflected that has escaped out through the stone. The bounding edge between the light and dark portion of the scale is distinct, and will give a direct reading of the refractive index of the stone under test. Since the glass of the instrument is always the same, the position of the shadow edge will entirely depend on the stone under test. Finally, the light rays pass into a glass prism which has the function of reflecting them, so that the scale can be conveniently viewed from above

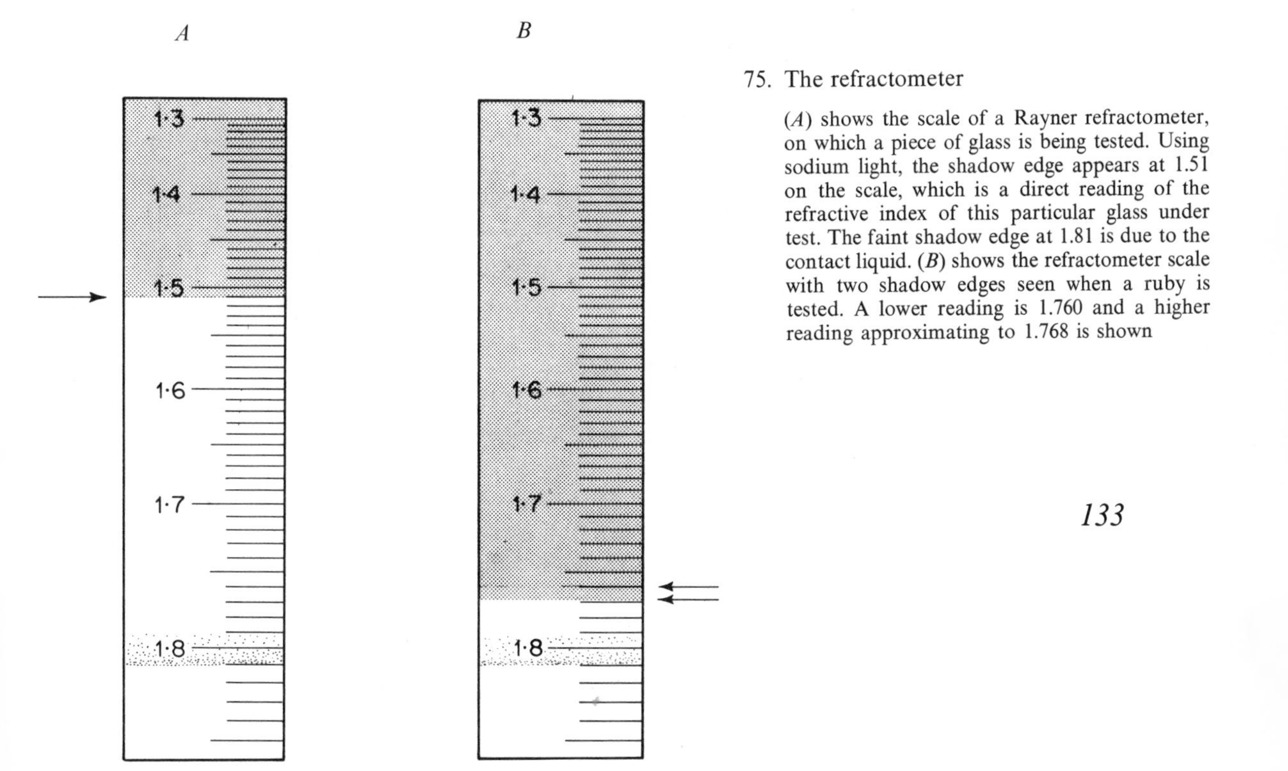

75. The refractometer

(*A*) shows the scale of a Rayner refractometer, on which a piece of glass is being tested. Using sodium light, the shadow edge appears at 1.51 on the scale, which is a direct reading of the refractive index of this particular glass under test. The faint shadow edge at 1.81 is due to the contact liquid. (*B*) shows the refractometer scale with two shadow edges seen when a ruby is tested. A lower reading is 1.760 and a higher reading approximating to 1.768 is shown

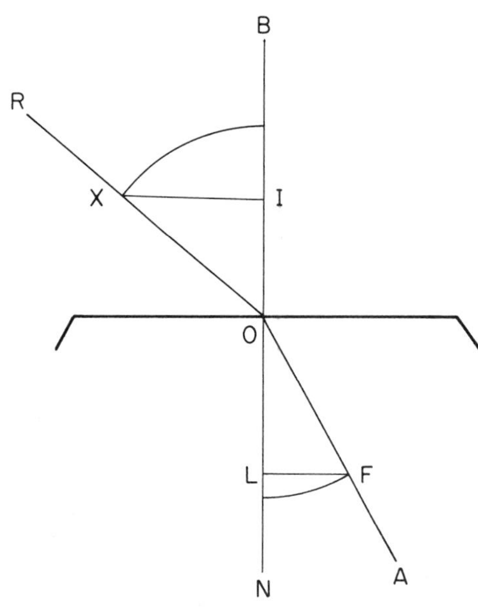

76. A geometrical explanation of the refractive index

RO is the incident ray and *OA* the refracted ray passing into the stone from air. Insert the point of a compass at *O*, where the incident ray strikes the surface of the stone, and, with any convenient radius, draw a circle cutting the incident ray at *X* and the refracted ray at *E*. Draw *XI* and *LF* perpendicular to the normal *BON*. The ratio $\frac{XI}{LF}$ will be constant whatever the angle of incidence, and this ratio equals the refractive index of the stone.

Let us now consider the two right-angled triangles *XIO* and *LFO*. The sine of the angle *XOI*, which is the angle of incidence, will be $\frac{XI}{XO}$. The sine of the angle *LOF*, which is the angle of refraction, is $\frac{LF}{OF}$. We now know that *OF* equals *XO*, since both are radii of the same circle.

Therefore:

$$\frac{\text{sine angle of incidence XOI}}{\text{sine angle of refraction LOF}} = \frac{XI}{LF} = \text{Refractive Index of stone}$$

rays will travel at different speeds through the stone and will each have a different refractive index. The refractometer is able to measure the refractive index of both light rays. If a tourmaline is tested on the refractometer, two distinct readings will result, one may be 1.62 and the other 1.638, showing us that there is a difference of 0.018 between the refractive indexes of the two rays. This difference is the amount of double refraction of tourmaline. To illustrate the practical usefulness of this method, imagine you are to identify a parcel of twenty red stones by means of this refractometer and the test shows:

Eight stones give two refractive index readings	1.76–1.77
Four stones give two refractive index readings	1.62–1.64
Eight stones give one refractive index reading	1.72

Referring to the tables on pages 149 to 155, the first eight stones are corundum (rubies), the next four are tourmaline, and the last eight are red spinels. More advanced books on this subject are given in the Bibliography.

Testing with a Spectroscope

In the first chapter, the subject of color in gem stones was discussed and how some stones would absorb certain wave lengths of light and allow others to pass. The *spectroscope* is an instrument designed to show with a high degree of accuracy which wave lengths have been absorbed. Its con-

77. Spectroscope, suitably arranged in a holder with gem stone in viewing position, and a powerful light source

struction is fairly simple. Inside a metal tube, three glass prisms are arranged as shown in Fig. 78. At one end of the instrument is an adjustable slit to allow light to enter. This slit can be opened and closed as required. The built-in glass prisms are designed to split the white light into its constituent colors and if a light is placed near the slit a continuous color band made up of the spectrum can be observed.

Imagine that the gem zircon is placed between the light source and the spectroscope. The lamp light must now first pass through the zircon before reaching the spectroscope. While passing through the stone, certain wave lengths of light are stopped. No longer will the undisturbed continous

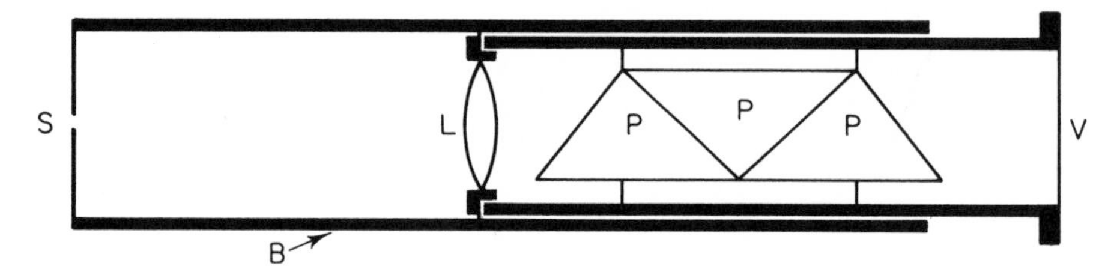

78. Simplified diagram of the direct-vision spectroscope

Light enters the spectroscope through a very narrow slit, *S* (colimator). Lens *L* brings the slit to focus for viewing purposes. Three glass prisms, *P*, are cemented into the brass tube, *B*. Their function is to split the white light into its spectrum colors. If a light source is placed near *S*, a continuous spectrum is observed through the eye piece at *V*

spectrum be seen. Instead, it will look as if somebody had drawn a mass of straight pencil lines vertically across the rainbow-colored band. This effect is known as the *absorption spectrum;* the lines are called *absorption lines.* If sunlight were viewed through the spectroscope, it would not give an uninterrupted spectrum; its absorption lines are due to elements occurring in the sun. It therefore cannot be used as a light source with the instrument.

In the case of zircon, it is believed that traces of radioactive substances form the absorption line pattern. This is so typical that it is unique to the gem stone (see Fig. 79). It also demonstrates how invaluable is an examination by spectroscope for the identification of some gem stones. No other stone will show an absorption spectrum like this one. If such a spectrum is seen, the stone under test must certainly be a zircon.

Many other gems have typical absorption spectra, and some of them are illustrated in Fig. 79. In many cases, these absorption spectra also form a valuable guide as to the composition of minerals. Various metals often cause dark bands, which vary in position according to the host mineral—hence their usefulness in identification. The narrow, fixed lines that can be seen in the absorption spectra of light coming from the stars are caused by the vapor of elements. These provide a valuable guidline to astronomers who seek to determine the composition of the stars.

The Microscope

The function of the microscope is to enlarge objects so as to make them more easily visible to the human eye. Its use in science is unlimited, and

Absorption spectrum of a zircon

Absorption spectrum of a ruby

Absorption spectrum of an emerald

Absorption spectrum of cobalt glass (blue glass)

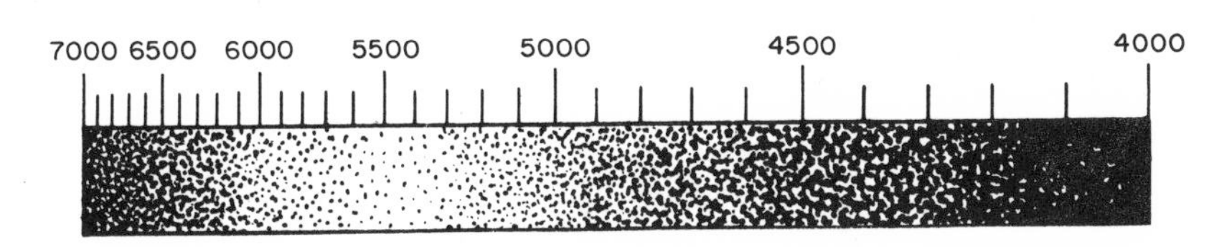

Uninterrupted spectrum with scale, indicating the approximate wave-lengths of various colors. *Note*:— These wave-lengths can be measured with great accuracy

79. Absorption spectra

to the gemmologist the microscope is more important than any other instrument. This is because one of the biggest problems in modern jewelry is the detection of synthetic and imitation stones, and without a microscope the task would be almost impossible.

The detection of imitation stones covers a vast field and the following lines serve only as an introduction. Three out of four of the most valued gem stones can be produced synthetically in the laboratory. These are the ruby, the sapphire, and the emerald. Needless to say, the difference in value between a natural and synthetic stone is enormous, and it is therefore of greatest importance to the jeweler that he can be sure they can be effectively distinguished from each other.

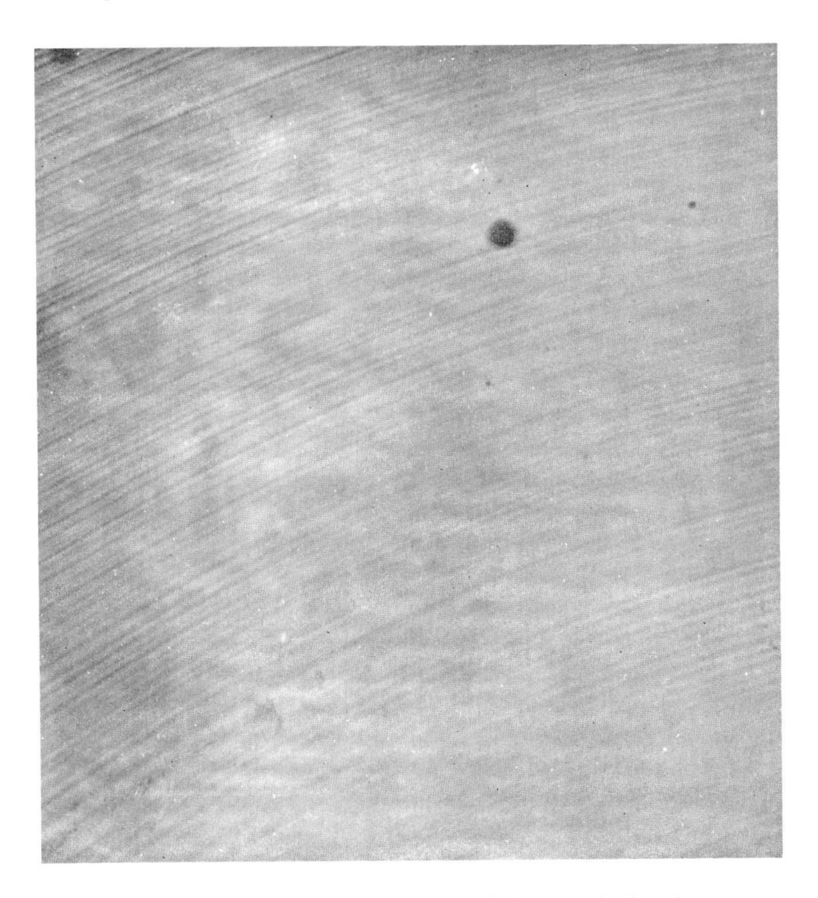

80. Typical curved growth lines and gas bubble in a synthetic ruby

Synthetic rubies made by the flame-fusion process are in all their physical properties almost identical with the natural stone. Chemically, both are crystalline aluminum oxide. The red color is in both cases produced by minute quantities of chromic oxide, and if synthetic and natural rubies are tested for their specific gravity, refractive index, and absorption spectra, the same results occur in both cases. Yet, if they are placed under a microscope, a marked difference between the two is found. What then are these internal telltale features that will enable us to distinguish the real from the synthetic?

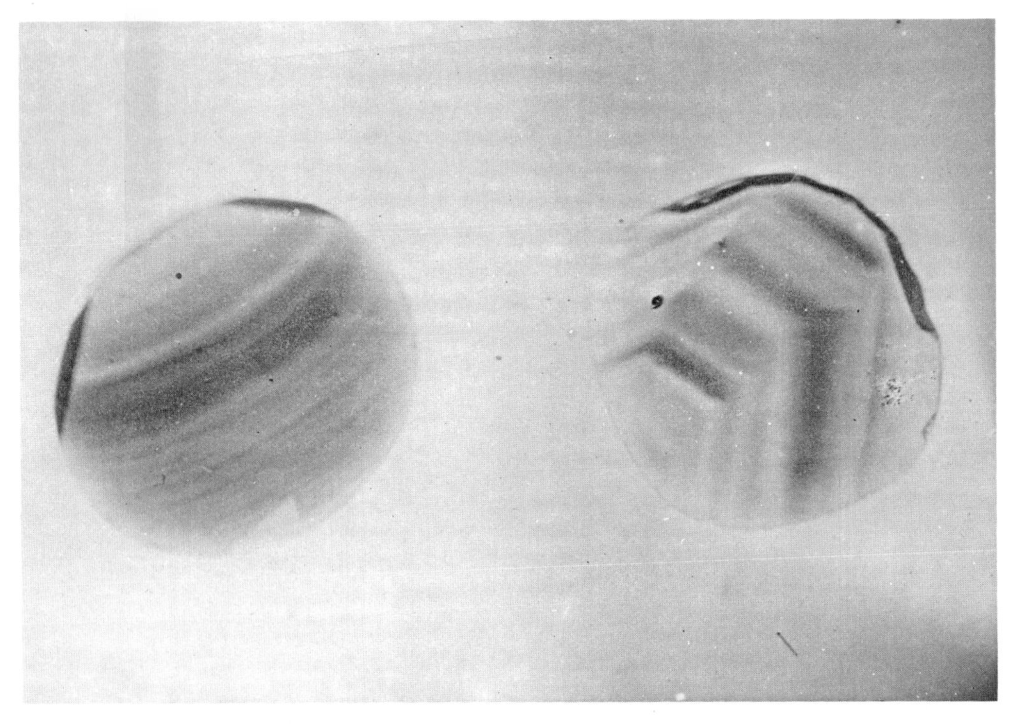

81. (Left) Synthetic blue sapphire showing typical curved bands; (Right) Natural green sapphire showing zoning (straight growth lines with definite angles)

Figure 80 shows the inside of a synthetic ruby, as seen under the microscope. Fine curved lines are immediately noticeable that are rather like the grooves of a phonograph record and run through the stone. There are also some black spots interspersed irregularly throughout the gem. The curved lines are known as growth lines, and they are produced during the formation of the synthetic boule and are a certain sign that the stone is synthetic. The black spots represent tiny bubbles of gas, and these, too, were included in the boule during its formation. Gas bubbles and curved growth lines are therefore typical characteristics of synthetic corundum.

But, what does the inside of natural corundum look like under the microscope? Side by side in Fig. 81 are a natural and synthetic sapphire. Again, there are the curved growth lines in the synthetic stone, but, in the natural one, the growth lines are straight and set at definite angles. This latter feature is an important characteristic of most natural mineral crystals. The microscope can provide all-important clues in the identification of rubies and sapphires.

A gem stone that may set an even bigger problem is the emerald. In this case, synthetic stones are internally also remarkably similar to the natural ones. Fortunately, Chatham's synthetic emeralds do have a lower specific gravity and refractive index than the natural stones, but it is not always

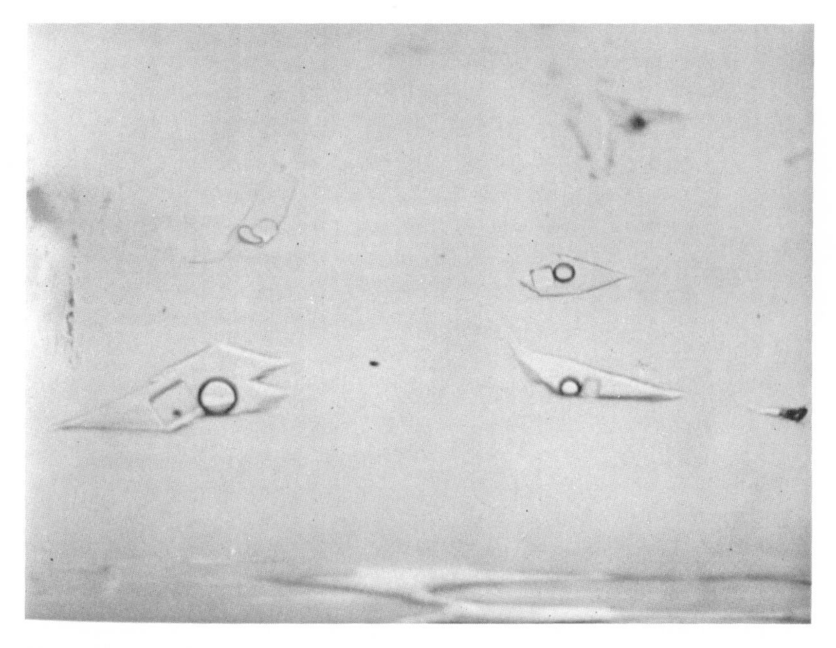

82. Cubic crystals in a three-phase inclusion in a natural Colombian emerald

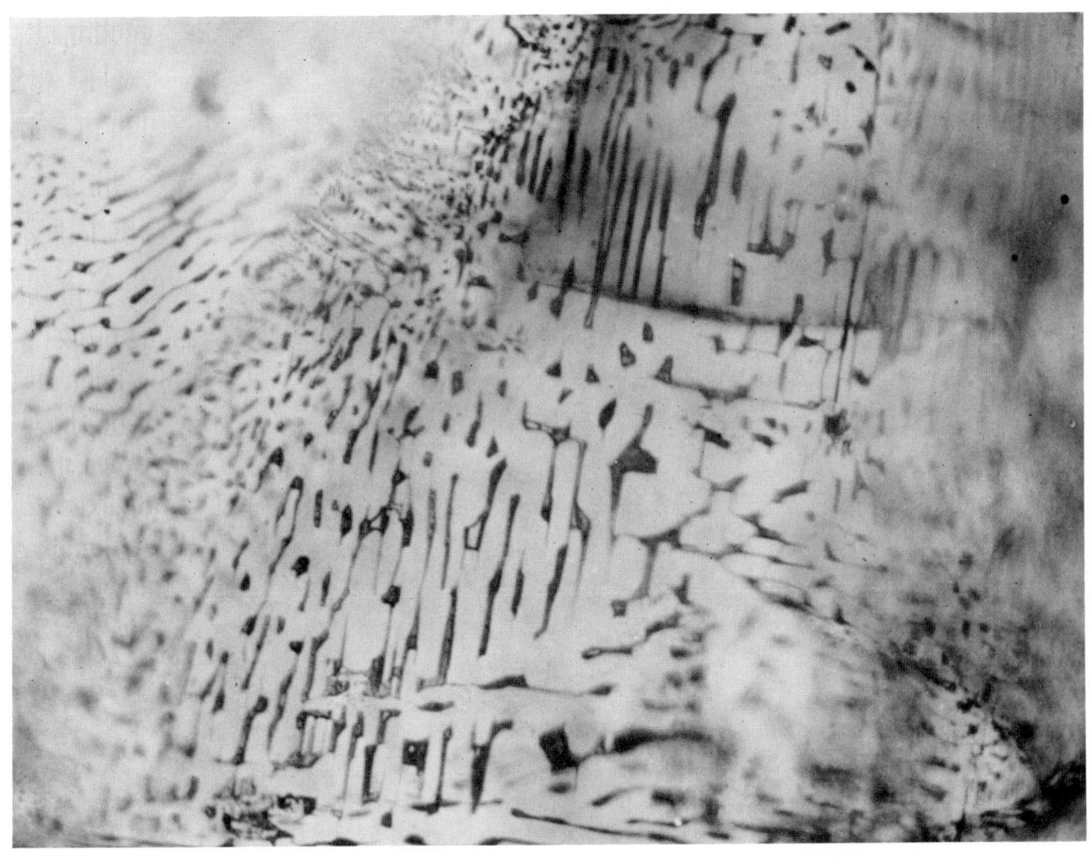

83. Enlarged view under the microscope of liquid-filled "feather inclusions" in an American synthetic emerald. These inclusions are a typical distinguishing characteristic of some of the synthetic emeralds produced in the United States

possible, if a stone is set in a piece of jewelry, to apply these tests. Here the microscope is useful again.

In Chapter IV, it was mentioned that the natural emerald possesses certain internal features called inclusions. Some of them take the form of spiky cavities filled with tiny mineral crystals and gas bubbles. Indeed, they are so typical that they can be associated with definite mining localities and thus form an important guide to the origin of some emeralds. Chatham's synthetic emeralds also possess special inclusions, and under the microscope, these look rather like a fine pattern of lace. They actually consist of minute interweaving channels filled with liquid and thus are very different in character from the inclusions of the natural emeralds.

The above are examples of but a few of the many useful functions the microscope can perform in gemmology. A simple magnifying glass that enlarges ten times can also be a valuable aid in the identification of some gem stones. Thus, a colorless zircon might well be confused with a real diamond, but if both are carefully examined with a hand lens by looking through the top of the stone at the rear facets, everything at the back of the zircon will appear double, thus revealing its strong light-splitting property.

Since a diamond belongs to the cubic crystal system, letting light rays pass through without splitting them, the double image will not be shown by it. This is one simple test that immediately distinguishes between these two gem stones. There is one direction along the so-called optic axis of a double-refractive stone where the light rays are not split and the doubling effect cannot be seen. It is therefore wise to tilt the gem a little when examining it with a lens to insure that the optic axis does not lie at right angles to the table facet.

Testing Pearls

In an industry that sells gems worth millions of dollars every year, there is a vital need for the accurate identification of natural, cultured, and imitation pearls. Elaborate scientific techniques have been evolved to test them.

A natural and a cultured pearl appear to be the same externally, since the coating deposited on the mother-of-pearl bead that forms the center of the cultured pearl resembles in most details the external features of the natural one. This coating may vary in thickness from ½ millimeter or less, to 2 millimeters, and experts used to handling natural and cultured pearls may be able to tell the difference by certain external signs, such as color, sheen, and markings, but, to make really sure, careful scientific tests must be applied. Perhaps one of the most ingenious instruments invented for this purpose is the *endoscope.*

The principle involved in its use is relatively simple. The most important part of the instrument is a hollow needle small enough to enter the drill hole

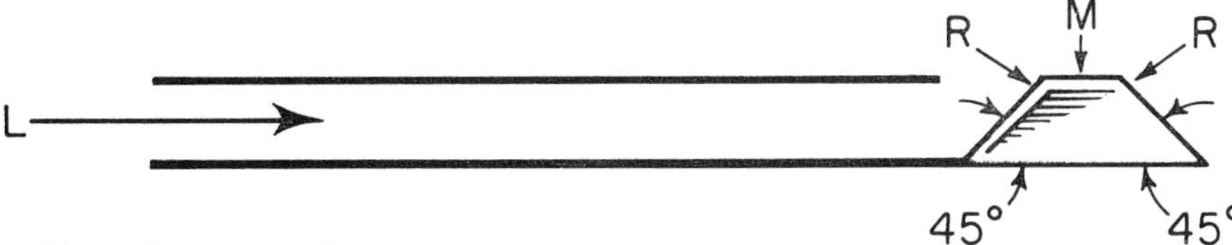

84. The endoscope needle

of a pearl. At the end of the needle a short metal rod (*M*) polished at either end to form two tiny mirrors (*R*) is fitted. These mirror ends are inclined toward each other. One of the mirrors forms one end of the needle, while opposite the other mirror there is a hole in the needle through which light (*L*) can pass (see Fig. 84). Imagine that a very powerful light is passed down the inside of the hollow needle. It will hit the mirror and be reflected out through the hole.

When a natural pearl is threaded on to the needle and is passed along it until the mirror arrangement comes to lie in the center of the pearl, a remarkable thing happens. The small beam of light (*L*) will travel from one mirror around the circular growth layers of the pearl to the other and be reflected out through the drill hole of the pearl at the other end (see Fig. 85*A*). An observer looking at the drill hole will see a tiny flash of light at *E* when the two mirrors are equidistant from the center of the pearl. The interior of a cultured pearl consists of a mother-of-pearl bead, and in such a bead the layers of growth are straight and not circular as in the natural

85. Testing of drilled pearls with endoscope. (*A*) is a cross-section diagram of a natural pearl; (*B*) is a cross-section diagram of a cultured pearl

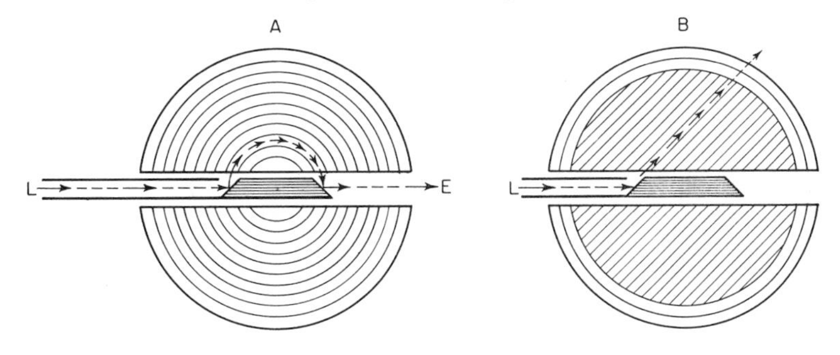

pearl. If a cultured pearl is passed along the needle the light entering at *L* is unable to reach the second mirror, and no flash is seen. Instead, it traverses the flat layers of the mother-of-pearl bead that forms the nucleus and can be seen as a streak of light on the surface of the pearl (see Fig. 85*B*).

Naturally, the endoscope can only be used for drilled pearls. There still remains the problem of how to test the undrilled ones. Here, the chief method used is x ray. This requires very special equipment, which can only be operated by a skilled technician. When cultured pearls are x-rayed, they will almost invariably show a clear-cut dark line around the circular margin of the mother-of-pearl bead (Fig. 86). The reason is that the oyster practically always secretes a thin layer of concholin around the bead before proceeding to add the layers of mother-of-pearl. It so happens that this layer of concholin is more transparent to x rays than the mother-of-pearl bead, and it will show up as a dark ring on the x-ray negative. The explanation is that x-ray negatives are in many ways similar to snapshot negatives. If negative film is too long exposed on a bright and sunny day, it will go black; in other words it will be overexposed.

This applies in much the same way to x-ray negatives. X rays differ from light rays in that they are invisible, and their wave lengths are much shorter than visible light, but they can penetrate through certain substances that

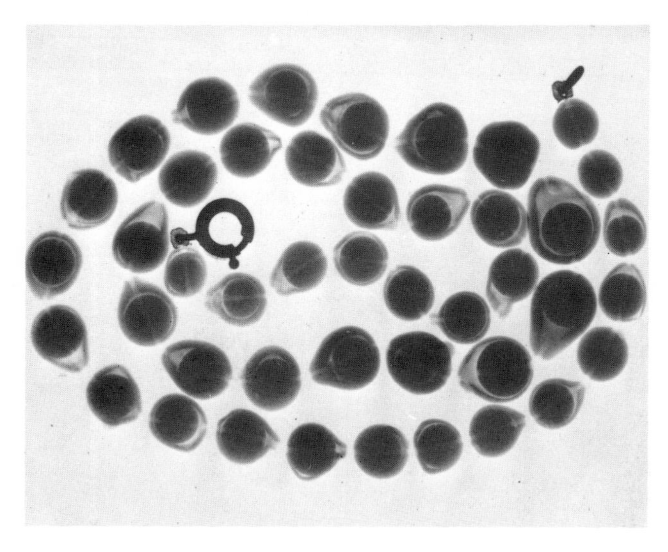

86. X-ray picture of a cultured pearl necklace. Note that in most of the cultured pearls the mother-of-pearl nucleus is surrounded by a thin layer of conchiolin shown on the photograph as a light ring. Remember that a dark ring on an x-ray negative will be a light ring on the positive print

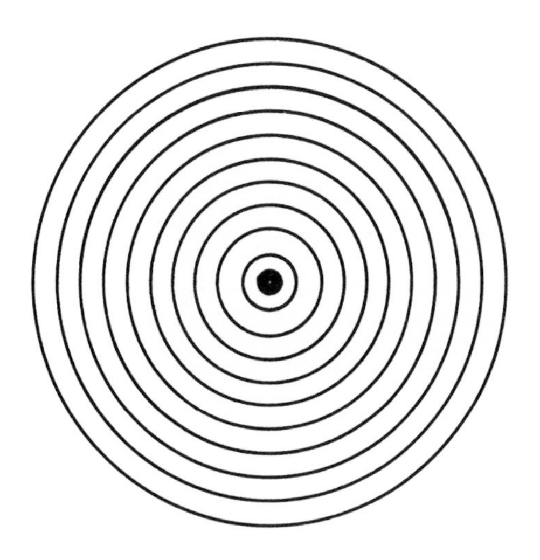

87. Diagram of cross-section of a natural pearl. The rings represent a few of the many layers from which a pearl is built up

visible light rays cannot. In the case of cultured pearls, more x rays penetrate through the layer of concholin than through the layer of mother-of-pearl, and, as negatives are darker when more visible light has fallen on them, so will x-ray negatives be darker where more x rays have fallen upon them.

Natural pearls, if x-rayed, will show more than one dark ring. In most cases, the natural pearl will show a whole series of dark rings throughout its structure because, as already pointed out, natural pearls are built up from large numbers of circular layers (see Fig. 88).

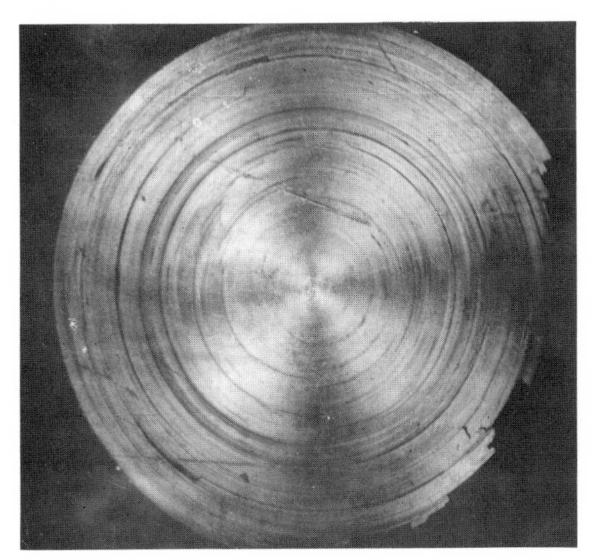

88. Thin section of a natural pearl, showing the circular growth layers

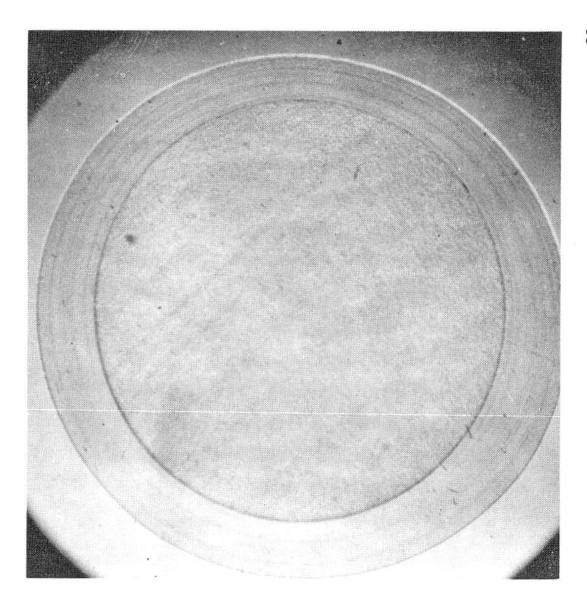

89. Thin section of a cultured pearl, showing the mother-of-pearl nucleus surrounded by circular growth layers

Some imitation pearls used to be made of small hollow glass spheres blown from opalescent glass, and lined on the inside with a substance known as "essence d'orient." This was made from the silvery scales of the bleak, a fish found in some European rivers. When the insides of the glass pearls had dried, they were filled with wax to give them weight and solidity. The modern imitation pearl consists of a solid glass bead with an external coating of pearl essence made from guanine crystals obtained from fish scales or synthetic lead salt.

A simple test can be applied to these imitations to distinguish them from natural and cultured pearls. If natural or cultured pearls are drawn gently across the teeth, they will feel distinctly gritty, while the glass imitations will feel quite smooth. This is because both natural and cultured pearls have tiny ridges all over their surface, whereas imitation ones are made from smooth glass.

This is but an introduction to some of the many interesting tests that can be applied to gems. New techniques are constantly being evolved to keep pace with the development of new kinds of synthetic gem materials and imitations. So long as mankind cherishes gems as something fine and desirable, the task will never end.

APPENDIXES

APPENDIX I

Gem Tables

NAME AND COMPOSITION	VARIETIES AND COLOR	HARDNESS
Diamond Carbon, C	Colorless highly transparent, yellow to brown, rarely blue, green, red. Bort—diamonds too poor for gem uses. Carbonado—opaque, gray, black	10
Corundum (*Ruby, Sapphire*) Aluminum oxide, Al_2O_3	Ruby—red Sapphire—blue, colorless, yellow, green Star rubies, Star sapphires	9
Beryl (*Emerald, Aquamarine*) Beryllium aluminum silicate, $Be_3Al_2(SiO_3)_6$	Emerald—grass green Aquamarine—pale blue, greenish blue Golden Beryl—yellow Pink Beryl—pink	7¾
Topaz Aluminum fluosilicate, $Al_2(F, OH)_2SiO_4$	Colorless, yellow to sherry colored, blue, rarely pink, red	8
Spinel Magnesium aluminum oxide, $MgAl_2O_4$	Red, brownish red, gray-blue, deep greenish, indigo, violet Ceylonite—black	8
The Garnet Group Calcium aluminum silicate, $Ca_3Al_2(SiO_4)_3$	Grossularite garnet—massive green Hessonite garnet (variety of grossularite)—yellowish red	7¼ 7¼
Magnesium aluminum silicate, $Mg_3Al_2(SiO_4)_3$	Pyrope garnet—deep red	7¼
Iron aluminum silicate, $Fe_3Al_2(SiO_4)_3$	Almandine garnet—deep purplish red	7¼
Manganese aluminum silicate, $Mn_3Al_2(SiO_4)_3$	Spessartite garnet—orange-red, yellow	7¼
Calcium iron silicate, $Ca_3Fe_2(SiO_4)_3$	Andradite—yellow, brown, green Demantoid garnet (variety of andradite)—bright green	6–6½

Specific gravity	Refractive index and double refraction (DR)	Occurrence
3.52	2.418	India, Brazil, South Africa, South-West Africa, Russia, United States, Congo Republic, Ghana, Sierra Leone, Tanzania, etc.
3.99	1.76–1.77 DR = 0.008	Rubies—Burma, Thailand, Ceylon Sapphires—Thailand, Burma, Ceylon, India, Australia, United States
2.6 to 2.8	1.57–1.58 DR = 0.006 Pink Beryl 1.58–1.59 DR = 0.008	Emerald—Colombia, Brazil, Egypt, Ural Mountains, Transvaal, Southern Rhodesia, India, Austria Aquamarine—Ural Mountains, Brazil, Madagascar, Ceylon, United States, India Pink Beryl—Madagascar, California, Brazil Yellow Beryl—United States, South-West Africa, Brazil
3.5 to 3.6	1.63–1.64 DR = 0.008 White and blue varieties 1.61–1.62 DR = 0.01	Brazil, Ceylon, Ural Mountains, California, Texas
3.60	1.72	Burma and Thailand with ruby, Ceylon gem gravels
3.45 to 3.55	1.72	Transvaal
3.65	1.74	Ceylon gem gravels
3.65 to 3.8	1.73 to 1.77	Czechoslovakia, South Africa with diamond in blue ground, Arizona, Ceylon
3.8 to 4.2	1.77 to 1.81	Ceylon, India, Madagascar, New York
4.16	1.80	United States, Brazil
3.85	1.89	Ural Mountains, Italy

NAME AND COMPOSITION	VARIETIES AND COLOR	HARDNESS
Tourmaline Complex silicate of boron and aluminum, with magnesium, iron, sodium, potassium, lithium present in varying quantities	Tourmaline containing iron—black Tourmaline containing magnesium—yellow, brown, black Tourmaline containing sodium, potassium, lithium—red, green or colorless	7¼
Peridot—Olivine Iron magnesium silicate, $(MgFe)_2SiO_4$	Green	6½
Zircon Zirconium silicate, $ZrSiO_4$	Reddish-brown, yellow, blue, colorless (High type) Various shades of green (Low type)	7½ 6½
Chrysoberyl Beryllium aluminate, $BeAl_2O_4$	Chrysolite—pale yellow to green yellow Alexandrite—green in daylight, red in artificial light Cymophane—Chrysoberyl cat's-eye	8½
THE QUARTZES *Crystallized Quartz* Silica, SiO_2	Rock crystal—colorless Amethyst—purple Citrine—yellow Cairngorm—brown Rose quartz—pink Quartz cat's-eye Tiger's-eye	7
Compact Quartz Silica with impurities	Jasper—brown, yellow, red, green Aventurine—green spangled, reddish-brown spangled	7
Cryptocrystalline Quartz Silica, SiO_2	Chalcedony—white (translucent) Plasma—dark green (opaque) Bloodstone—green spotted with red (opaque) Chrysoprase—fine green (translucent) Carnelian—orange red (translucent) Agate—concentric bands in various colors Onyx—black and white bands Sardonyx—red and white bands Moss agate—white or gray with black or green markings Mocha stone—gray with red or black markings	7

Specific gravity	Refractive index and double refraction (DR)	Occurrence
3.05	1.62–1.64 DR = 0.018	Brazil, California, Madagascar, Ceylon, South-West Africa
3.34	1.65–1.69 DR = 0.036	St. John's Island (Red Sea), Burma, Queensland, Arizona, Hawaii, New Mexico, and other localities
4.69 4.0 to 4.5	1.92–1.98 DR = 0.059 1.80 DR = None	Ceylon gem gravels, Vietnam, Thailand
3.71	1.74–1.75 DR = 0.009	Chrysolite—Brazil, Ceylon Alexandrite—Ural Mountains, Ceylon, Brazil Cymophane—Ceylon gem gravels, Brazil
2.65	1.54–1.55 DR = 0.009	Rock Crystal—very wide distribution but especially Brazil, Madagascar, Alps, United States, Canada Amethyst—Brazil, Uruguay, India, Ceylon, Mexico, Arizona Cairngorm—Scotland, also in many other parts of the world Cat's-eye—Europe Tiger's-eye—South Africa
2.65 variable	1.54 variable	Jasper—wide distribution Aventurine—India, China, Brazil
2.65 variable	1.53 variable	White chalcedony—Brazil, United States, Mexico Chrysoprase—Australia, Germany Carnelian—India, South America Moss agate—mainly India Mochastone—Mocha (Red Sea) Other varieties widely distributed all over the world

Name and composition	Varieties and color	Hardness
Opal Silica with a variable percentage of water	Common opal—no play of color; transparent to opaque; green, yellow, brown, etc. White Opal } Black Opal } Fire Opal—reddish-orange	5½ to 6½
Turquoise Hydrous phosphate of aluminum and copper	Iranian—fine deep blue Egyptian—greenish-blue United States (Arizona, New Mexico)—pale blue to green	6
The Jades		
Nephrite Calcium magnesium iron silicate	Dark green, also white and lighter shades of green	6–6½
Jadeite Sodium aluminum silicate, $NaAl(SiO_3)_2$	Pale gray, light green, apple green, emerald green, mauve, brown, orange, and so on	6½–7
The Feldspars Silicates of aluminum and either potassium, sodium, or calcium		
Orthoclase Potassium feldspar, $KAlSi_3O_8$	Moonstone—most important of the group as a gemstone. Colorless, milky-blue sheen Amazonstone—green to bluish-green Orthoclase—yellow, transparent	6–6½
Plagioclase—mixtures of: Sodium feldspar, $NaAlSi_3O_8$ and Calcium feldspar, $CaAl_2Si_2O_8$	Sunstone—reddish spangled Labradorite—gray with shimmering color effect	
Lapis Lazuli Complex silicate containing sulfur	Blue; opaque Brassy specks of pyrites frequently present	5½
Sphene Calcium Titanium silicate $CaTiSiO_5$	Yellow, green, brown Strong dispersion (fire)	5
Spodumene Lithium Aluminum Silicate $LiAl(SiO_3)_2$	Kunzite—lilac, pink Hiddenite—green	7
Fluorspar Calcium fluoride CaF_2	Green, yellow, pink, purple, colorless, brown Blue John—massive banded	4

Specific gravity	Refractive index and double refraction (DR)	Occurrence
2.1 Fire Opal 2.0	1.45	Common opal—Brazil, Australia, United States, etc. White Opal and Black Opal—Australia (Queensland, New South Wales), Hungary Fire Opal—Mexico
2.6 to 2.8	—	Iran, Egypt, New Mexico, Arizona, Nevada
2.96 to 3.1	1.62	Eastern Turkestan, New Zealand, Alaska, Wyoming, California, British Columbia
3.33 to 3.35	1.66	Upper Burma, Mexico
2.5 to 2.7	approx, 1.53	Moonstone—Ceylon, India Amazonstone—India, Brazil Orthoclase (yellow)—Madagascar Sunstone—Norway, Canada, India Labradorite—Canada, Finland
2.5–2.9	1.5	Badakshan area of Afghanistan, Lake Baikal (Siberia), Chile
3.45–3.56	1.90–2.02 DR = 0.134	Austria, Switzerland, Mexico, Brazil, United States
3.18	1.66–1.68 DR = 0.015	Kunzite—California, Brazil, Madagascar Hiddenite—North Carolina (source now exhausted)
3.18	1.434	British Isles, Norway, South-West Africa, United States Blue John—Derbyshire, England (supplies exhausted)

APPENDIX II

Conversion Table

The weight unit used for weighing gem stones is the carat.
1 carat = $\frac{1}{5}$ gram = 0.2 gram

The weight unit used for weighing pearls is the pearl grain.
1 pearl grain = $\frac{1}{4}$ carat = 0.05 gram

WEIGHT IN CARATS	WEIGHT IN GRAMS
0.1	0.02
0.2	0.04
0.3	0.06
0.4	0.08
0.5	0.10
0.6	0.12
0.7	0.14
0.8	0.16
0.9	0.18
1.0	0.20
1.25	0.25
1.5	0.30
1.75	0.35
2.0	0.40
2.5	0.50
3.0	0.60
3.5	0.70
4.0	0.80
4.5	0.90
5.0	1.00
5.5	1.10
6.0	1.20
6.5	1.30
7.0	1.40
7.5	1.50
8.0	1.60
9.0	1.80
10.0	2.00

APPENDIX III

DISTRIBUTION OF DIAMOND WORKERS (OTHER THAN MINING) THROUGHOUT THE WORLD, 1965

Antwerp	14,000
Israel	8,000
India	8,000
United States	3,500
Germany	1,500
Amsterdam	600
United Kingdom	650
South Africa	650

GLOSSARY

GLOSSARY

ABSORPTION SPECTRUM. When light that has passed through a transparent, colored solid, such as a gem stone, is viewed through a spectroscope, the resultant spectrum, or color band, will no longer be continuous but will have dark bands that cross it vertically. These bands mark wave lengths of light which have been absorbed by the gem. The recognition of absorption spectra patterns is an important means of gem identification.

ALUMINA. The oxide of aluminum (Al_2O_3).

ANGLE OF INCIDENCE. The angle between the path of the incident light ray and the normal to a reflecting surface, such as a mirror, at the point of incidence; *see* normal.

ANGLE OF REFLECTION. The angle between the normal and the path of a reflected light ray.

ANGLE OF REFRACTION. The angle through which the light ray is bent or refracted as it passes from a rarer medium, such as air, to a denser medium, such as a gem stone.

ARCHIMEDES' PRINCIPLE. The concept that when a body is totally or partially immersed in a fluid it experiences an upthrust equal to the weight of the fluid displaced. The apparent loss of weight of a totally immersed body is equal to the weight of water it displaces.

ATOM. The smallest part of an element that retains its physical and chemical properties.

AUTOCLAVE. An electrically heated pressure chamber used in the manufacture of synthetic emeralds.

BLUE EARTH. Marine sediment in the eastern Baltic, of Tertiary age, which is mined commercially for amber. Actually, "blue earth" looks black when wet and dark with a greenish tinge when dry.

BLUE GROUND. A basic igneous rock forming the so-called diamond *pipes* in South Africa. On the surface, blue ground is weathered by oxidation to yellow ground.

BOMB. *See* autoclave.

BOULE. The rounded crystal column of synthetic corundum or spinel produced under the inverted oxyhydrogen blow pipe of a Verneuil Chalumeau.

BRILLIANT CUT. The most popular cut; it gives a diamond maximum fire. A brilliant-cut diamond has 58 facets; 33 in the crown and 25 in the base.

BRUTING. An intermediate step after cleaving and sawing a diamond crystal before its facets are polished. The stone is mounted on the chuck of a turning lathe and a second diamond pressed against it. The lathe rotates at about 400 revolutions per minute, and the gem is ground to its rough finished outline. Also called girdling.

CABOCHON CUT. In the *simple* version of this cut, the stones have a curved top and a flat base. In the *double* style, stones have both upper and lower portions curved.

CARAT. The unit of weight now universally adopted for gem stones. One carat equals one-fifth of a gram.

CARBONADO. An opaque, massive black variety of diamond, frequently crystalline to granular, or compact and without cleavage, which is used in industry.

CENTIGRADE SCALE. A temperature scale on which the freezing point of water is zero degrees and the boiling point of water is 100 degrees.

CENTRIFUGAL CASTING. A method of casting cheaper types of jewelry in which molten metal is pressed by centrifugal force into a plaster mold.

CLEAVAGE. Crystals cleave in certain definite directions related to their patterns of symmetry along cleavage planes lying parallel to a potential or actual crystal face. For example, the cleavage of a diamond is octahedral; that is, it is parallel to an octahedral face of the crystal.

CLEAVING. A method of splitting a diamond crystal along one of its cleavage planes.

COLOR ABSORPTION. Different substances have the power to absorb varying wave lengths of light, and the color of a gem or of any material is determined by the wave lengths of light that are not absorbed by the substance.

COMPACT QUARTZ. These quartzes consist essentially of an aggregate of tiny grains packed together into massive lumps containing as much as 20 per cent of foreign matter in the form of clay, iron oxide, and other impurities. Jasper is an example.

COMPOUND. Two or more elements combined in a definite numerical ratio with bonds between their atoms that can be split only by a chemical change.

CONCHIOLIN. A cartilaginous organic compound that forms the outer layer of an oyster shell. It is also one of the constituents of the pearl.

CONTACT LIQUID. Sulfur-saturated methylene iodide. A thin film of this liquid of high refractive index ensures optical contact between the dense glass of the refractometer and the gem being tested.

CORUNDUM. Hexagonally (trigonally) crystallized oxide of aluminum (Al_2O_3).

CRYPTOCRYSTALLINE. A term used to describe the structure of certain mineral substances made up of masses of tiny crystals, for example, the quartz varieties grouped under the general title of chalcedony.

CRYSTAL. A solid substance in which the atoms are arranged in a definite and repetitive pattern. As a result of this regular atomic arrangement, crystals have plane faces and definite external geometrical shapes.

CRYSTAL AXES. Imaginary lines of reference used to define a crystal system and to describe the relative positions of the crystal faces. There are usually three, and at the most four, such axes, which all intersect in the crystal's center.

CRYSTALLIZED QUARTZ. A quartz group normally comprising transparent crystals that show definite crystal forms. Examples of this group are rock crystal, citrine, and amethyst.

CRYSTAL SYSTEM. One of seven main symmetry groups into which all crystals can be classified; *see* cubic crystal system, hexagonal crystal system, monoclinic crystal system, orthorhombic crystal system, tetragonal crystal system, triclinic crystal system, and trigonal crystal system.

CUBIC CRYSTAL SYSTEM. A system whose forms can be invested with three crystal axes of equal length intersecting at right angles.

DIAMOND POLISHING. Unlike other gem stones, diamonds are cut and polished in one operation, which is carried out on polishing laps. These are special horizontal porous cast-iron disks measuring about a foot in diameter and half an inch in thickness, charged with a small amount of diamond dust mixed with olive oil, and rotating at 2,500 revolutions per minute.

DIAMOND POWDER. Lower quality industrial diamonds, known as bort, which are crushed and graded into mesh sizes to be employed in grinding wheels, cutting saws, and boring tools.

DICHROISM. Colored crystals belonging to crystal systems other than the cubic crystal system often appear to change color when viewed from different directions. This effect, also known as *pleochroism* (in crystals not tetragonal or hexagonal), is a directional property of crystals closely bound up with the crystal structure.

DIRECTIONAL PROPERTY. This is related to the internal atomic structure of a crystal, which usually exhibits different physical properties in different directions. Thus, for example, a diamond can be split easily in any plane parallel to a crystal face of its octahedron form. Green tourmaline crystals may be opaque in one direction, yet transparent in another. A knowledge of the directional properties of gem minerals is of great importance to the lapidary and the diamond cutter.

DISPERSION. The power of a gem, or any other transparent medium, to separate light into its spectrum colors. The colorful sparkle or fire of the diamond derives from its high degree of dispersion. When cut into gem stones, colorless corundum (white sapphire) and rock crystal lack this fire because of their relatively low power of dispersion.

DOP. A brass cup filled with solder (1 part of tin to 3 parts of lead) mounted on a copper stalk. It is used in diamond polishing; the gem is embedded in the solder to be held during the polishing process.

DOUBLE REFRACTION. When a ray of light enters a crystal belonging to any system other than the cubic one, it is generally split up into two refracted rays, each proceeding at a different velocity along a different path. Known also as *birefringence,* this phenomenon is of great importance in testing gems.

DRY DIGGINGS. A term applied to certain South African diamond mines because of their arid surroundings.

ELEMENT. A substance that cannot be altered by a chemical change so that it is split into any simpler chemical substance. For example, gold, carbon, and oxygen are elements.

ELECTRUM (*White Gold*). A term used in antiquity for a naturally occurring gold and silver alloy. The "white gold" of American jewelers is decolorized by the addition of the metal palladium.

ENAMEL. Used as jewelry decoration, it consists largely of powdered glass of various colors fused to a metallic base.

ENDOSCOPE. An instrument designed to distinguish between drilled natural and drilled cultured pearls.

ENGINE TURNING. A method for engraving metals in jewelry making. Modern machines fitted with diamond-cutting tools produce attractive light effects by engraving several parallel lines simultaneously.

ESSENCE D'ORIENT. Made from the silvery scales of the bleak, a fish found in some European rivers, it is used to make imitation glass pearls.

FILIGREE. Fine wires soldered on to a solid background to form patterns and designs. Known since about 2500 B.C., this method of decorating metals is still practiced today.

FIRE. The colorful flash of light produced from the facets of a cut stone; it is due to the splitting of white light into the spectrum colors; *see* dispersion.

FLAME FUSION PROCESS. The process invented by Verneuil to manufacture synthetic corundum and spinel.

FLUORESCENCE. The light effect which is the response of certain minerals to the exposure to invisible radiation, such as ultraviolet light or x rays.

GEM GRAVELS. Gravels and sands deposited in layers and terraces, usually by the action of running water. They consist of a multitude of different materials, a proportion of which are gem minerals.

GRANULATION. Decorative patterns made by minute grains of gold soldered to a gold background. Known since about 2500 B.C., the process died out around A.D. 1000, but was revived again in our time.

GREASE TABLES. Galvanized iron trays covered with a thick coating of grease, they are designed to separate diamond crystals from other mineral substances. The crushed rock mixture containing diamond crystals is washed over grease tables, which are constantly jiggled. The diamonds adhere to the grease while other materials are washed away with the water.

GROWTH LINES. Fine curved lines in synthetic rubies, they are visible with a lens or a microscope. These lines are produced during the formation of a synthetic ruby boule. Synthetic blue sapphires normally show curved broad bands of color, which sometimes can be seen with the unaided eye.

The presence of curving lines or color bands is a sure sign that the stone is synthetic. In natural stones the growth lines are straight with definite angles.

GUANINE CRYSTALS. Obtained from fish scales, they are a constituent of pearl essence and, mixed with a paintlike carrier, they form the external coating of glass imitation pearls.

HABIT. A mineral may crystallize in a number of different crystal forms. Its most characteristic form is termed its "habit." Thus diamond is often found in the form of the octahedron and so is described as being of octahedral habit.

HARDNESS. The amount of resistance set up by the surface of a gem stone or other solid substance when an attempt is made to scratch it with another stone or object.

HEAT TREATMENT. Certain gem minerals (citrine quartz and zircon are good examples) may change color when careful heat treatment is applied. Brazilian amethyst, the purple variety of quartz, produces yellow-brown or red-brown stones when heated. The yellow-brown topaz from the Ouro Preto district in Brazil will change to rose pink when heated to a little below dull red heat. Reddish-brown zircon crystals found in Vietnam may become colorless, blue, or golden after heat treatment. Other stones affected by heating are some green beryls, which turn sky blue, and certain dark green tourmalines, which may turn to emerald green.

HEAVY LIQUIDS. Liquids with a high density suitable for determining the specific gravity of gem stones. The most useful liquids are: *Bromoform:* specific gravity 2.9. Colorless when fresh, turning brown on exposure to sunlight. It can be diluted with benzene or toluene to cover a wide range of intermediate densitities. *Methylene iodide:* specific gravity 3.33. A pale brown liquid that darkens almost to black on exposure to light. Like bromoform, it can be diluted with benzene and toluene to cover a wide range of intermediate densities. *Clerici Solution:* A saturated solution of thallium malonate and thallium formate. Specific gravity at room temperature is about 4.15, but it can be diluted to any required extent with distilled water, and reconcentrated by gentle warming. This liquid is corrosive and poisonous and should only be used under controlled conditions in a laboratory.

HEXAGONAL CRYSTAL SYSTEM. Crystal forms of this system have four crystal axes. Three of the axes are equal in length and intersect their centers at angles of 60°. The fourth vertical axis is unequal and lies at right angles to the plane formed by the other three.

HOLLOW CABOCHON. Stones curved above the girdle and hollowed out below the girdle to increase transparency and lighten the color. Indian almandine garnet is frequently cut in this style.

HYDROSTATIC WEIGHING. A method of determining the specific gravity of a solid by a direct weighing technique.

IDIOCHROMATIC MINERALS. Minerals in which the color is due to some essential chemical constituent. For example, the color of peridot is green due to the presence of iron in its basic formula $(MgFe)_2SiO_4$, whereas turquoise is blue, because of copper.

INCLUSIONS. Small cavities, tiny bubbles of gas, mineral crystals, or other foreign matter trapped within a crystal when it was originally formed. Inclusions are a guide to the origin of a gem stone and enable natural stones to be distinguished from their synthetic counterparts.

INTERFERENCE OF LIGHT. When two light systems of the same wave length and vibrating in phase are forced to travel the same path, one wave of their wave length and phase, but of an intensity equal to their combined intensities, is produced. Conversely, two wave systems of the same wave length, but out of phase by half a wave length, forced, by polaroid, into traveling along the same path will mutually destroy one another and darkness ensues. Rays of white light, which consists of many different wave lengths, traveling out of phase, produce the vivid color effects known as interference; this creates the shimmering colors of the pearl, and the film of oil on water.

LAPIDARY. A craftsman engaged in gem cutting. The term is normally not applied to a diamond cutter.

LAWS OF REFRACTION (*Snell's Laws*). (*a*) For two given media and light of one wave length, the ratio of the sine of the angle of incidence to the sine of the angle of refraction is constant. (*b*) The incident and refracted rays and the normal at the point of incidence lie in one plane.

LIGHT. According to the wave or undulatory theory, light consists of electromagnetic waves that emanate from a luminous source in all directions in straight lines.

MANTLE. An oyster is contained in two flaps of tissue known as mantle flaps.

These line the two valves (shells) of the animal. This mantle is covered with minute cells able to produce horny, organic material (conchiolin), and the calcium carbonate that builds up the oyster shell and, under specific circumstances, may produce a pearl.

MECHANICAL DOP. A mechanical device fitted with adjustable claws that has partly replaced the more conventional solder dop.

METAL. An element possessing characteristic luster. A good conductor of heat and electricity; with few exceptions, metals are malleable and ductile and can thus be worked into shape by hammering or by pulling into wire.

MOHS' SCALE. A hardness scale devised by Friedrich Mohs, the German mineralogist, in 1822. He arranged ten minerals in order of their ability to resist scratching, thus:

Diamond (the hardest natural substance on earth)	10
Corundum	9
Topaz	8
Quartz	7
Feldspar	6
Apatite	5
Fluorspar	4
Calcite	3
Gypsum	2
Talc	1

The scale gives only an indication of the order of hardness and has no quantitative significance.

MOLECULE. The smallest part of an element or compound that can exist as a free and separate substance, yet retain all the chemical properties of the substance.

MONOCLINIC CRYSTAL SYSTEM. Crystal forms of this system have three unequal crystal axes, one at right angles to the other two that intersect obliquely.

NACRE (*Mother of Pearl*). The iridescent layer made up of tiny overlapping plates of calcium carbonate that form the inside lining of oyster shells. This layer is also an essential part of the surface of the lustrous pearl.

NORMAL. A perpendicular to a reflecting surface constructed at the point at which the incident ray strikes the surface.

ODONTOLITE, OR BONE TURQUOISE. Fossil bones and teeth colored blue or green by iron phosphate.

OPTIC AXIS. A direction of single refraction in a double refractive gem stone. There is one such direction in all crystals belonging to the tetragonal, hexagonal, and trigonal crystal systems. Such crystals are termed uniaxial. Crystals belonging to the orthorhombic, triclinic, and monoclinic crystal systems have two directions of single refraction, and are termed biaxial.

ORTHORHOMBIC CRYSTAL SYSTEM. Crystal forms with three crystal axes unequal in length and at right angles to each other.

PARTICOLORED. A term applied to an individual crystal exhibiting different colors. Tourmaline crystals are often particolored, one half being pink and the other half green.

PEARL GRAIN. A unit of weight used in the calculation of the price of pearls; 4 pearl grains = 1 carat.

PERIOSTRACUM. The outer horny layer of an oyster shell made from a substance called conchiolin. Normally it is only produced by the edge of the mantle.

PIEZOELECTRICITY. An electrical effect shown by certain crystals. When physical pressure is applied to a crystal slab, it induces opposite electrical charges on reverse faces. Conversely, a thin crystal slab can be made to oscillate if placed into an alternating electric field.

PIPE. A vertical, cylindrical mass of volcanic substance in which diamonds occur.

POLISHING LAP. *See* diamond polishing.

PRECIOUS. A somewhat arbitrary term normally applied to some gems: diamond, ruby, emerald, sapphire, and pearl.

PRISMATIC LAYER. A part of the shell of the pearl oyster. Minute prisms of calcium carbonate lie at right angles to the surface of the shell. This layer is normally produced by the mantle edge only.

PROFILE CUT. A new style of diamond cut first introduced by A. Nagy in 1961.

REFLECTION OF LIGHT. A ray of light striking a mirror or any other polished surface is reflected in accordance with the following laws: (*a*) the angle of incidence is equal to the angle of the reflection; (*b*) the incident ray, the reflected ray, and the normal all lie in one plane.

REFRACTION OF LIGHT. When a ray of light passes from air into an optically denser medium, such as a gem stone, its speed is lessened. The ray will no longer follow its original path but is bent to follow a direction more nearly perpendicular to the surface between the two media.

REFRACTIVE INDEX. A numerical value describing the refracting power of a medium. The refractive index of a medium equals

$$\frac{\text{Velocity of light in air}}{\text{Velocity of light in the medium}}$$

Or the refractive index equals $\frac{\text{Sine angle of incidence}}{\text{Sine angle of refraction}}$. In practice, air is taken as a standard of comparison, and assigned a refractive index of 1.

REFRACTOMETER. An optical instrument designed to measure the refractive indexes of gem minerals and other substances. It is a very useful and accurate means of identifying gem stones.

REPOUSSÉ. Ornamental work produced on sheet metal by means of a hammer and punch.

RIVER DIGGINGS. A term applied to excavations along the Orange and Vaal rivers during the first South African diamond rush.

SEMIPRECIOUS. A term formerly applied to gems other than those referred to as precious, or decorative, stones.

SILICA GLASS. The amorphous product of the fusion of crystalline quartz by an intensely hot oxyhydrogen flame.

SILK INCLUSIONS. Parallel bundles of fine fiberlike crystals or cavities that give a silky sheen by reflected light. This effect is observable in star rubies and star sapphires.

SINE OF AN ANGLE. In a right-angled triangle, the side opposite the right angle is called the hypotenuse. The sine of an angle is the ratio of the side opposite that angle to the hypotenuse.

SINGLE REFRACTION. When a ray of light passes through a crystal belonging to the cubic crystal system, its speed is lessened; consequently, it is bent from its original path, and it emerges as a single ray. All gems belonging to the cubic crystal system, as well as noncrystalline materials such as glass, are singly refractive.

SPECIFIC GRAVITY. The specific gravity of a substance is defined as the ratio:

$$\frac{\text{Weight of substance in air}}{\text{Weight of an equal volume of pure water at } 4^\circ \text{ centigrade}}.$$

SPECTROSCOPE. An instrument incorporating a system of glass prisms or a ruled grating that resolves light into its spectrum colors.

SPECTRUM. Ordinary white light is a complex mixture of colored light. When a narrow beam of white light, sunlight, for example, is passed through a glass prism, the light is drawn out into a long colored band consisting of the colors violet, indigo, blue, green, yellow, orange, and red. This is known as the visible spectrum.

STAR STONES. Stones that may exhibit a four- six- or twelve-rayed star of light when cabochon cut in a manner allowing the inclusions within the stone—which cause this light effect—to lie parallel to the lateral axis of the stone and at right angles to the vertical axis.

STEP OR TRAP CUT. The facets above and below the girdle lie parallel to a rectangular table facet. Used mostly for colored stones but more recently also for diamonds. To produce the most pleasing effect, proportions depend on the individual stone.

SYNTHETIC EMERALD. Manufactured emeralds of similar chemical composition and crystal structure as the natural stones. Both the refractive index and the specific gravity of Chatham's synthetic emeralds are lower than that of the natural stones. The internal markings, inclusions, of synthetic emeralds also differ from those of the natural stones.

SYNTHETIC RUBY. A manufactured ruby usually made by the Verneuil process, with essentially the same chemical composition and properties as the natural stone. The raw material used in its manufacture is pure alumina powder to which is added 2½ per cent chromic oxide to produce the red color of the ruby.

SYNTHETIC SAPPHIRE. A manufactured sapphire made by the Verneuil process having essentially the same chemical composition and properties as the natural stone. White sapphire consists of pure alumina without any coloring oxide. Most white sapphires are synthetic in origin; blue sapphires are produced by the addition of titanium oxide and iron oxide to the alumina.

TETRAGONAL CRYSTAL SYSTEM. Crystal forms with two crystal axes of equal length intersecting at right angles and a third principal axis that intersects the other two at right angles and is either longer or shorter than the other two.

TRICLINIC CRYSTAL SYSTEM. Crystal forms of this system have three crystal axes, unequal in length, intersecting obliquely. They are: a vertical axis; a shorter horizontal axis running from back to front, called the brachyaxis; and a longer horizontal axis running from right to left called the macroaxis.

TRIGONAL CRYSTAL SYSTEM. This crystal system has axes identical with those of the hexagonal one. In the latter, the principal axis is one of sixfold symmetry, while in the trigonal system the principal axis is one of threefold symmetry.

TURQUOISE MATRIX. Turquoise interspersed with dark veins of limonite—stained rock.

ULTRAVIOLET RAYS. Invisible rays not much shorter in wave length than visible violet rays.

VALVES. The two shells enclosing the soft body of an oyster.

VERNEUIL CHALUMEAU. An apparatus invented for the manufacture of synthetic corundum by the Frenchman, A. Verneuil, early in this century.

WAVE LENGTH. The distance between the crests of two successive waves. Light waves are measured in *Ångström units.* One Ångström measures one ten-millionth of a millimeter in length. The wave lengths of visible light range from about 7,500 Å in the red part of the spectrum, to 3,900 Å in the violet part of the spectrum. Beyond 7,500 Å lie the still longer and invisible infrared and radio waves, and beyond 3,900 Å lie the shorter and invisible ultraviolet rays, X rays, gamma rays, and cosmic rays.

X RAYS. Electromagnetic radiation first observed by W. C. Roentgen in 1895. X rays affect photographic film in a manner similar to light and are able to pass through many solid substances with comparatively little absorption. With a mean value of about 1 Ångström, the wave length of x rays is considerably shorter than that of light.

ZONING. Straight growth lines of bands with definite angles often seen in natural corundum crystals. If present in gem stones, this is an indication that the stone is of natural origin.

BIBLIOGRAPHY

BIBLIOGRAPHY

ANDERSON, B. W. *Gem Testing.* 7th ed. London: Heywood and Company Ltd., 1964.

BALL, S. H. *A Roman Book on Precious Stones.* Los Angles: Gemological Institute of America, 1950.

BÖRNER, R. *Minerals, Rocks and Gemstones.* London: Oliver and Boyd Limited, 1962.

DAKE, H. C. *The Art of Gem Cutting.* 6th ed. Spokane, Wash.: J. D. Simpson & Co., 1956.

EVANS, J. *A History of Jewellery: 1100–1870.* London: Faber & Faber Ltd., 1953.

GÜBELIN, E. J. *Inclusions as a Means of Gemstone Identification.* Los Angeles: Gemological Institute of America, 1953.

HUGHES, G. *Modern Jewellery.* London: Studio Books, 1963.

HIGGINS, R. A. *Greek and Roman Jewellery.* London: Methuen & Co. Ltd., 1961.

KRAUS, E. H., and SLAWSON, C. B. *Gems and Gem Materials.* New York: McGraw-Hill Book Company, 1947.

KUNZ, G. F. *The Magic of Jewels and Charms.* Philadelphia and London: J. B. Lippincott Co., 1915.

LIDDICOAT, R. T. *Handbook of Gem Identification.* 6th ed. Los Angeles: Gemological Institute of America, 1962.

SHIPLEY, R. M. *Dictionary of Gems and Gemology.* 4th ed. Los Angeles: Gemological Institute of America, 1948.

SINKANKAS, J. *Gem Cutting.* 2nd ed. Princeton: D. Van Nostrand Co., Inc., 1963.

———. *Gemstones of North America.* Princeton: D. Van Nostrand Co., Inc., 1959.

SMITH, G. F. H., and PHILLIPS, F. C. *Gemstones.* 13th ed. London: Methuen & Co. Ltd., 1962.

SPENCER, L. J. *A Key to Precious Stones.* London: Blackie & Son Limited, 1946.

SPERISEN, F. J. *The Art of the Lapidary.* Milwaukee: Bruce Publishing Co., 1961.

WEBSTER, R. *Gems: Their Sources, Descriptions and Identification.* Butterworth & Co. (Publishers) Ltd., 1962.

WEINSTEIN, M. *The World of Jewel Stones.* New York: Sheridan House, 1958.

INDEX

INDEX

R

S

About the Author

P. J. Fisher was educated at the Beltane School in Wiltshire, England, and later continued with London University studies. He is now Managing Director of an industrial concern in the United Kingdom. A student of natural history, Mr. Fisher is a Fellow of the Gemmological Association of Great Britain and a Fellow of the Royal Society of Arts. He is married and has a daughter.